THE
EARTH
PAST & PRESENT

McGRAW-HILL EARTH SCIENCE PAPERBACK SERIES

Richard Ojakangas, Consulting Editor

THE
EARTH
PAST & PRESENT

RICHARD W. OJAKANGAS

Professor of Geology
University of Minnesota, Duluth

DAVID G. DARBY

Associate Professor of Geology
University of Minnesota, Duluth

McGRAW-HILL BOOK COMPANY

New York   St. Louis   San Francisco   Auckland   Düsseldorf   Johannesburg
Kuala Lumpur   London   Mexico   Montreal   New Delhi   Panama
Paris   São Paulo   Singapore   Sydney   Tokyo   Toronto

This book was set in Helvetica by Black Dot, Inc.
The editors were Robert H. Summersgill and Carol First;
the designer was J. E. O'Connor;
the production supervisor was Judi Allen.
The drawings were done by J & R Services, Inc.
R. R. Donnelley & Sons Company was printer and binder.

THE EARTH: PAST AND PRESENT

1 2 3 4 5 6 7 8 9 0 D O D O 7 8 3 2 1 0 9 8 7 6

Library of Congress Cataloging in Publication Data
Ojakangas, Richard W
  The earth, past and present.

  (McGraw-Hill earth science paperback series)
  Includes index.
  1. Geology. I. Darby, David G., date, joint
author. II. Title.
QE28.037   550   75-45172
ISBN 0-07-047676-4

CONTENTS

THREE

FOUR

FIVE

SIX

PREFACE

The Earth—Past and Present is a book specifically designed for a liberal education introductory course in geology. It is the outgrowth, in large part, of our own frustrations in teaching Introductory Geology at the University of Minnesota, Duluth. Most of the available books are indeed good, but somewhat unsatisfactory for a truly liberal education course because they are generally too long, too detailed, too laden with technical terminology, and written in "too stiff" a style. We think that undergraduates whose futures are in nonscientific fields can become disinterested by these features, and as geologists we would like everyone to learn about and enjoy this fascinating field of study.

Thus we have attempted to make this a brief book, but one which still presents the important concepts and facts. We feel that this brevity, coupled with the style of writing and abundant illustrations and photographs, will not only make geology seem less formidable to nonscientists but will help them to better appreciate and retain the main concepts and facts. This brevity should also make it more convenient for instructors to expand upon topics of their expertise and choice.

We hope we have succeeded in attaining these goals and, at the same time, not limited the body of essential data necessary for those who would become geologists.

ACKNOWLEDGMENTS

Several people assisted us in the preparation of this book. Robert Heller and Barry Haskell reviewed preliminary versions and offered several excellent suggestions which we've incorporated into the text. Bob Summersgill, Editor, and Carol First, Editing Manager of this project, kept us, within broad limits, on schedule. Ken Moran took several photos and made black and white photos from dozens of slides. Jackie Gollinger typed most of the manuscript, and Phyllis Parkinson typed part of an earlier version. Our families patiently put up with our long hours, and we patiently put up with the advice and grief given us by our colleagues in the Department of Geology, University of Minnesota, Duluth. To all we express our sincerest appreciation.

Richard W. Ojakangas
David G. Darby

THE
EARTH
PAST & PRESENT

ONE

THE EARTH—
THE BIG PICTURE

EARTH'S PLACE IN SPACE

People long ago observed that the sun rises in the east and sets in the west and that the moon and stars appear to do the same. Therefore, wasn't it just common sense to think that the sun, moon, and stars revolve around earth (Figure 1-1), the center of the visible universe? Most people agreed, but as early as 400 B.C., some Greeks thought that the earth was not the center of things. Plato, in his old age, reportedly "repented of having given the earth the central place in the universe, which did not belong to it"; some have implied that he also was leaning toward a sun-centered system.

However, in A.D. 140, Ptolemy of Alexandria wrote an encyclopedia of astronomy in which he reiterated that the earth was the stationary center of the universe. In effect he said, "If the earth did have motion of its own . . . birds and objects thrown into the air would be left behind while the earth moved away from beneath them." Unbelievably, this was the believable word until 1543 (for 1400 years!), partly because this earth-centered concept of the universe was strongly supported by the church.

In 1543, a Polish astronomer named Copernicus stated in his *Concerning the Revolutions of the Heavenly Spheres*, "In the center of all rests the sun. For who would place this lamp in another or better place than this, wherefrom it can illuminate everything at the same time? How exceedingly fine is the God-like work of the Best and Greatest artist." His ideas were not readily accepted; Martin Luther called him a fool, as did many bishops and cardinals.

Figure 1-1 Earth as viewed from the moon. *(NASA photograph.)*

When in 1609 Galileo saw with the newly invented telescope four moons circling Jupiter, he had proven to his own satisfaction that the earth, with only one moon, was not the greatest body in space and certainly not the only center of rotation. These findings, coupled with Galileo's abrasive personality, alienated church authorities, and the Inquisition finally forced him to abandon his celestial studies and admit that he had erred.

About the same time, Kepler in northern Europe discovered the essential laws of movement of the planets in our solar system, and in 1664, Newton unified astronomy when he came forth with his universal law of gravitation: Every particle of matter in the universe attracts every other particle with a gravitational force. Today this is stated by the equation

$$F = \frac{Gm_1m_2}{d^2}$$

This equation shows that the force of attraction between any two bodies is determined by multiplying the gravitational constant (G) times the mass of the first body times the mass of the second body and dividing by the square of the distance between their centers. Much later, in the early 1900s, Einstein refined the astronomical relationships with his theory of relativity.

The ideas of Copernicus, Galileo, and Kepler, establishing the sun rather than the earth as the center of the solar system, have been collectively referred to as the "first intellectual revolution in science."

OUR SOLAR SYSTEM

The first six planets—Mercury, Venus, Earth, Mars, Jupiter, and Saturn—have been known for thousands of years, for they can be seen with the naked eye (Figure 1-2). Earth has been known the longest. Uranus and Neptune, the next farthest planets from the sun, were observed in 1781 and 1846, respectively.

In 1901, Piazzi, an Italian astronomer, spotted a new body in space and watched it for 41 days, finally concluding it was a member of our solar system. But then it was "lost" and no one, not even Piazzi, could spot it, which proved very embarrassing, for he had publicly announced his find. But Gauss, a 22-year-old German student, came to his rescue. He used Piazzi's 41 days of observation to calculate the path of the body, thereby locating the lost "planet" again. It proved to be a very small "planet" (Ceres), only 772 kilometers in diameter, the largest of the planetoids or asteroids. Now more than 30,000 others are known, of which only 21 are greater than 160 kilometers in diameter. They move in an orbit between Mars and Jupiter, and probably are either the remains of an exploded planet or material that never coalesced into a single planet.

In 1914, astronomer Percival Lowell of the United States, on the basis of a wobble in Uranus's orbit, correctly predicted the presence of the most distant planet, Pluto, as well as its size, speed, and location. However, it took 16 years more to actually spot it. In 1974, some astronomers thought they had evidence for a new planet beyond Pluto, but this has been disputed.

Hundreds of millions of meteoroids, most very small with a mass of less

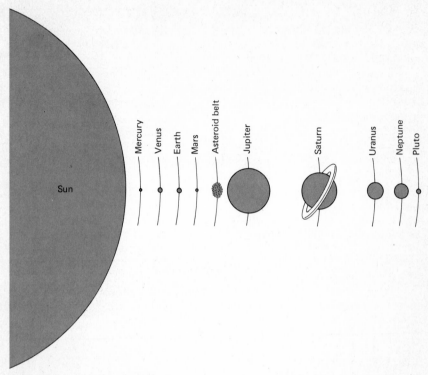

Figure 1-2 Our solar system. The relative sizes and positions of the sun and the planets are shown, but the planets are so far from the sun that it is impossible to draw the interplanetary distances to scale.

than 1 gram, enter the earth's atmosphere each day. At night these "shooting stars" are visible as they "burn up" and ionize the atmosphere through which they pass. They probably originate in the asteroid belt. With all those meteoroids, is the earth safe? At least one person, a woman in Alabama, was hit by one; it came through the roof of her rented house and hit her in the thigh while she was taking a nap. When universities wanted to buy the meteorite, her landlord claimed it. After a long lawsuit, the courts declared that the woman who had been hit by it was the rightful owner.

The earth has a dozen known big astroblemes, or "star wounds," plus another dozen probables, each apparently the result of the collision of a large meteorite with the earth. The most famous is Meteor Crater in Arizona; it is 1200 meters in diameter and more than 180 meters deep (Figure 1-3). Why isn't the earth covered with meteorite craters, as is the moon? Could it have been bombarded as much as the moon, but the scars mostly obliterated by the earth's surface processes, especially those related to the earth's water and atmosphere?

So we are one small planet in a solar system (Figure 1-2) composed of one fair-to-middling star only 1,400,000 kilometers (864,000 miles) in diame-

(a)

(b)

Figure 1-3 Meteor Crater, Arizona, viewed from an altitude of about 6.4 kilometers (4 miles) and from nearby. *(Closeup photo courtesy of Yerkes Observatory.)*

ter, 9 planets, 31 moons, 30,000+ asteroids, and countless comets, dust, molecules, and atoms. As you know, our solar system is mostly space. If the sun were the size of a basketball, earth would be about the size of the head of a pin and would be located 81 feet away, and Pluto would be 0.61 miles away. (The nearest other star on this scale would be more than 4000 miles away; its light takes 4.21 years to reach us, and light travels at about 300,000 kilometers, or 186,000 miles, per second!)

And this is but one solar system in one galaxy, or "star cluster," the Milky Way, which consists of an estimated 100 billion stars. And there might be a billion galaxies! Might not some of these other stars have planets, too? All stars are too far away for us to see any planets in orbit around them, but photographs taken of Barnard's star (the fourth nearest star to our sun) over the past 35 years have recently been interpreted to record a "double wobble" in its path, which may be due to the gravitational attraction of nearby planets.

Although our sun is only an average star, it radiates the energy which keeps our earth warm, drives the circulation of air and water, and sustains all life. Yet we are a small speck 150 million kilometers (93 million miles) from the sun and receive only about 1/2,200,000 of the sun's energy. That is fortunate, for each square meter of the sun's surface radiates 15 million calories of energy per second—enough to make all our oceans, streams, and rivers boil. (Some large stars give off as much energy in 6 days as our star does in 1 million years, and some have diameters 2700 times larger than our star.) The temperature at the sun's surface is estimated at more than 5500°C, and nearly 14 million °C at its center. The sun derives its energy by nuclear fusion of hydrogen, forming helium, a process described briefly in the next chapter. As the sun consists of more than 80 percent hydrogen (most of the rest is helium), it should continue to shine for a long time to come.

All the planets revolve about the sun in the same direction as the earth does, and most spin, or rotate in the same direction. Obviously, the planets closest to the sun are hotter and those farthest away are very cold; the earth has it just right.

The four inner planets—Mercury, Venus, Earth, and Mars—compared with the outer planets, are small and heavy with few satellites. Their densities range from 3.95 to 5.52, as compared with the density of water of 1.0. Earth is the heaviest of the four, and its moon has a density of 3.3. All four inner planets are hard or "rocky" bodies. In contrast, the densities of the large outer planets range from 0.70 for Saturn to 1.7 for Uranus; these planets are probably in part gaseous. Pluto has an estimated density of about 4.0 and is thus a way-out oddball.

Earth is unique in several ways. For one thing, it contains abundant water and could indeed be called the "water planet." It also has the only nitrogen-oxygen atmosphere known. Mercury is too close to the sun to have an atmosphere, and our moon is so small that it hasn't enough gravity to hold an atmosphere. Venus and Mars have CO_2-rich atmospheres. Jupiter has an atmosphere of hydrogen, helium, methane, and ammonia; it is giving off 2.5 times as much heat as it receives from the sun, and it may be in effect a small star which never really got its nuclear furnace going properly. Saturn, Uranus, and Neptune may have atmospheres of methane and ammonia.

The features which Galileo was the first to see on the moon—craters, shadows of walls and mountains, and "seas," or maria—have now been observed firsthand by the astronauts. Many old speculations about the moon have been discarded. These have included some as strange as a walled and fortressed city existing in a mare, the craters being the result of bomb explosions when the moon was used as an atom-bomb target range, and the craters being coral reefs on the maria floors.

We now know about the moon's volcanic plateaus, channels due to flowing lava, chains of volcanic craters, countless meteorite craters, and irregularly shaped and cratered mountainous uplands. We have sampled rocks which are not too unlike earth's rocks, especially those which originate from the cooling of molten rock. The moon has had a history of meteoric cratering all through time and also has had two or more periods of volcanism. We have found, on the basis of radiometric age dating, that some moon rocks are older than any found on earth. Since the moon and the earth are so closely related in space and may well have had a somewhat common early history, the old age of the moon (perhaps as old as 4.6 billion years, based upon interpretations of materials brought back to earth by the Apollo astronauts) may also serve as a likely date for earth's origin. Independent age determinations of meteorites indicate a similar time of origin. And we know that the moon lacks water and is therefore quite unlike its close relative, earth.

Photographs of Mars taken by Mariner 9, which circled the planet twice daily for months and months between 1971 and 1973, have provided us with an amazing array of Martian knowledge. They revealed volcanoes on Mars which dwarf those on earth; one is three times as high as our highest mountain. Volcanic rocks clearly cover more than half the planet. Mars has a "Grand Canyon" of its own which is four times as deep as ours, and several others which probably equal our Grand Canyon in size. Meandering "valleys," which now appear to be dry, are suggestive of a past surface water supply. (The straight "canals" of Mars, long thought to be evidence of life on that planet, proved to be optical illusions.) Meteorite craters are abundant. Dust storms are commonplace, as are fields of "sand dunes," both the result of winds. Clouds are present in Mars's thin atmosphere. Polar "ice caps," which advance in the winter and retreat in the summer, are thought to be largely carbon dioxide ice rather than water ice. Thus Mars, while quite different from earth and the moon, also has gross similarities to them. Some scientists think that Mars may be in an intermediate stage of planetary evolution, perhaps somewhere between the moon and the earth.

So much for the rest of the solar system. Let's get on with our study of earth, the planet we know best.

EARTH'S SHAPE AND SIZE
We're used to hearing that the earth is round, yet it looks quite flat. The astronauts, of course, verified that it was round by bringing back photographs of earth taken from the moon (Figure 1-1). Yet there still exists a Flat Earth Society of unbelievers in a round (spherical) earth.

Columbus was not the first to say the earth was round. As early as 500 B.C. the Greeks had correctly ascertained the earth's shape. How? Mainly by observing the shape of the earth's shadow on the moon during eclipses of the moon, ships coming into sight on the horizon (mast tip first, then mast and sails, then entire ship), and mountains becoming totally visible as travelers moved closer and closer to them.

Eratosthenes, a Greek in Egypt, in 250 B.C. calculated the size of the earth. He reasoned that because the sun always appears the same size to people, regardless of where they happen to travel, it is very distant from earth and its rays are therefore essentially parallel lines of light when they hit the earth. He reasoned further that as the sun's reflection was seen in the bottom of a deep well at noon on a certain day in Syene (now Aswan), the sun must be directly overhead. On the same day to the north in Alexandria, the sun's rays made an angle of about 7° with a vertical column as determined by the length of the column's shadow. Knowing the distance between Syene and Alexandria, based on the rate of travel of camel caravans, he calculated that the distance between the two points was an arc equivalent to about one-fiftieth of a full circle. Eratosthenes thus established a circumference for the earth which was surprisingly close to today's accepted value of about 40,000 kilometers (25,000 miles).

In the mid-1600s, Newton suggested that the force of the earth's rotation was powerful enough to cause a bulge on the equator. With the newly invented pendulum clock and a decent telescope, the vertical angle of a single star could be quite accurately measured from different spots on the earth's surface at the same instant. The length of the arc between two stations could thus be measured and the length of a single degree of arc (1/360 of a circle) could be determined. The latter length varied somewhat at different locations; if the earth were a sphere, a degree of arc should always have the same length. A pendulum clock, the rate of which will be affected by gravity, was found to run slower in French Guiana, South America, than in Paris. Using Newton's equation for the force of gravity (see above), we see that the only factor in the equation which can vary is the distance between the center of the pendulum and the center of the earth. As this distance increases, the force of gravity (F) between the earth and the pendulum would decrease, thereby causing the pendulum clock to run slower than one closer to earth's center. Therefore, earth's gravity in French Guiana must be less than in Paris. We now know that the earth's polar diameter is about 12,710 kilometers (7900 miles) and the earth's equatorial diameter is about 44 kilometers longer (7927 miles). Thus, the earth is not a perfect sphere. Nevertheless, it is still rounder than a bowling ball.

EARTH'S MASS, INTERIOR, AND MAGNETIC FIELD

Can we weigh the earth? While difficult, it is not impossible. Weight and mass are related by the equation $W = gm$, where g is the strength of gravitational attraction. So once g and m are known, the weight can be calculated. Actually, the weight itself is a rather meaningless number—who cares how heavy the earth is? The *density*, or mass per unit volume ($d = M/V$), is a much more useful number, and it can be calculated easily once earth's mass is known.

Cavendish in England in the late 1700s, again using Newton's law of gravity ($F = Gm_1m_2/d^2$), solved for the gravitational constant (G) in laboratory experiments by using two small metal spheres as the two masses. Once G was known, then the equation could be solved again with a metal sphere representing one mass, the earth representing the other mass, and the earth's radius as the distance (d) between the two masses. Thus, earth's mass has been determined to be about 6×10^{27} grams, or 5.52 grams for each cubic centimeter of earth volume. As 1 cubic centimeter of water weighs 1 gram, and thus has a density of 1.0, earth is 5.52 times as heavy as water and thus has a density of 5.52. The common rocks on earth's surface have densities of only 2.7 to 3.0 grams per cubic centimeter. Then why is the earth so dense?

The density data suggest, of course, that the earth must have a heavy interior in order to have an average density greater than the density of surface rocks. But direct observations of materials at depth within the earth are obviously impossible. The deepest mines penetrate only the outer 3 or 4 kilometers of earth's crust, and the deepest oil wells are less than 9 kilometers deep. As the earth's radius is about 6370 kilometers, you can see that we have barely scratched the surface. But fortunately we have indirect evidence on the nature of earth's interior, based on the movement of earthquake waves through the earth. This evidence, which is discussed in more detail in Chapter 3, shows that the earth is made of several layers, with the densest material at the center. Three main layers, or zones, have been distinguished—a thin rocky *crust*, a thick rocky *mantle*, and a thick metallic iron (with some nickel) *core*.

The earth has a magnetic field (Figure 1-4) and, simply speaking, acts as if it had a giant bar magnet in its interior. The interior of the earth, however, appears to be too hot for the magnetism to be the result of permanently magnetized material. Iron loses its magnetism at 760°C (1400°F) and nickel at 349°C (660°F). On the basis of measurements in deep wells, we know that the

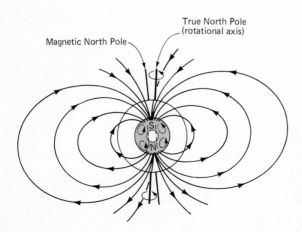

Magnetic North Pole

True North Pole (rotational axis)

Figure 1-4 Earth's magnetic field. The field behaves somewhat as if it were caused by a gigantic bar magnet (as drawn), but it is probably the product of eddies in the molten outer core (shaded area).

temperature near earth's surface increases about 1°C for every additional 30 meters of depth; if this rate continued to earth's center, the temperature there would be more than 200,000°C. We don't think that this is the actual temperature, but surely it is hotter in the core than the melting point of iron, about 2000°C.

If the earth's core cannot be a permanently magnetized material, then what causes the field? The evidence suggests a deep-seated internal origin for this magnetic field, and scientists now believe that the magnetism emanates from the earth's outer core, which may be liquid and may be generating the field as eddies of molten material move by thermal convection. In effect, the earth is acting as a gigantic dynamo, converting mechanical energy into electrical energy, thereby creating the electromagnetic field. The moon's magnetic field, by comparison, is 1000 times weaker than earth's; this suggests that the moon lacks a molten core.

EARTH'S ATMOSPHERE, HYDROSPHERE, AND LITHOSPHERE

Earth's inorganic surface regime consists of three regimes, or "spheres"— the atmosphere, hydrosphere, and lithosphere.

The *atmosphere*, the gaseous envelope with its life-sustaining molecules, extends from the surface upwards more than 10,000 kilometers to the level at which the hydrogen density is equal to that in interplanetary space. However, 90 percent of the atmosphere is within 18 kilometers of the surface, and 99.9 percent is within 50 kilometers. Earth's gravitational attraction, of course, is instrumental in holding the atmosphere. Besides providing the oxygen so necessary for life, the atmosphere is instrumental in soil-forming processes and in the formation of some rocks as well. Important stuff.

The *hydrosphere* is the liquid realm. On earth it consists of water. Of this water 97 percent is in the oceans. The remaining 3 percent is fresh water, of which 77 percent is tied up in glacial ice, 22 percent is underground in soil and rocks, and only about 1 percent is in lakes and rivers. (If all the water vapor in the atmosphere were condensed, it would form a layer on earth only a few centimeters thick.) Like the atmosphere, the hydrosphere is basic to all life and is a factor in the formation of soils. Water is also important in the histories of many types of sedimentary rocks, those rocks which are formed at the surface. It, too, is important stuff.

The *lithosphere* is the solid realm which makes up the continents and the floors of the ocean. Most of this book deals with the lithosphere and processes affecting the lithosphere, and so no more need be said here except that it consists of rocks, which are made up of minerals. Technically, it consists of the crust and the uppermost part of the mantle, extending to a depth of approximately 100 kilometers.

EARTH'S SURFACE FEATURES

The primary relief features on the earth's surface are the continents and the ocean basins. The continents have an average elevation of about 850 meters above sea level; the deep ocean basins have an average depth of about 4000 meters. The oceans, which cover 71 percent of earth's surface area, are in reality somewhat larger than the ocean basins, for they lap up onto the continents. These zones of overlap, known as the continental slopes and shelves, are actually parts of the continents. With this taken into consideration, the continents constitute 35 percent of earth's surface area. The continents are not distributed completely at random; nearly every point on land has an opposite point in the sea on the other side of the earth. We don't know why.

Secondary relief features on the continents are the *mountains*, the *plateaus*, and the lower-lying *plains*. These will be described in detail later in this book. Hills and valleys are minor features.

Secondary relief features beneath the oceans (Figure 1-5) include the gently sloping (less than 0.1°) *continental shelves*; the *continental slopes*, with general inclinations of 3 to 6° (but which locally may be much steeper); and the *deep ocean basins*, which comprise the deeper parts. The junction of the slope and the deep ocean basin is commonly covered with a gently sloping *continental rise*, a thick wedge of sediment which has been moved down the slope and deposited there. Commonly the continental rise consists of a series of huge coalescing subsea fans, with each fan located at the lower end of a *submarine canyon* cut into the continental slope. One example of such a canyon is Hudson Canyon on the slope off the Hudson River of New York; it is comparable in size to the Grand Canyon (Figure 1-6).

The rises merge with the *abyssal plains*, areas of nearly horizontal sea floor, which clearly are the result of deposition of sediment that moved down the slopes and across the continental rises and buried a previous rugged topography. *Seamounts* are peaks which project upward 1000 meters or more from the deep ocean basin floors; some project through the sediments

Figure 1-5 Diagrammatic representation of major features beneath the ocean at the edge of a continent. The vertical scale is exaggerated; the continental shelves are *very* gently inclined surfaces and most continental slopes have inclinations of only 3 to 6°. No horizontal scale is given, for the shelf varies in width from a few kilometers to a few hundred kilometers. Water depths also vary, but general figures are about 200 meters at the outer edge of the shelf, 2000 meters at the base of the slope, and as much as 10,000 meters in the deeper parts of the ocean basins.

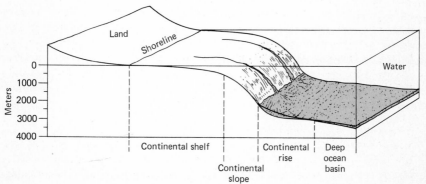

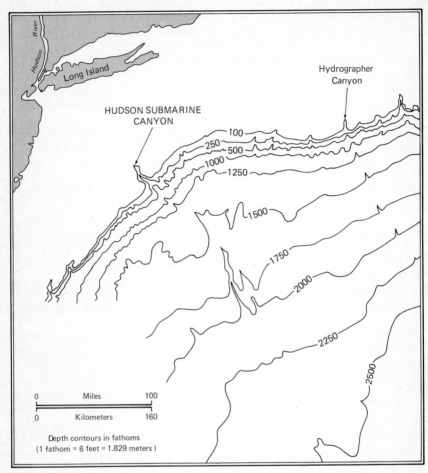

Figure 1-6 Generalized chart of Hudson Submarine Canyon, located off the coast of New York and on line with the Hudson River. Note several smaller canyons also cutting slope. *(After B. C. Heezen, Marie Tharp, and Maurice Ewing, 1959, Geological Society of America Special Paper No. 65.)*

of the rise. The 20,000 or so seamounts are evidently submarine volcanic peaks. Some, with their tops eroded to broad, flat surface, are called *guyots*. The deepest parts of the ocean floors are elongate and narrow *trenches* (Figure 1-7); the deepest, 10,860 meters below sea level, is the Marianas trench. Landward of the trenches are volcanic *island arcs*, or more rarely, volcanic arcs on the adjacent continents. Why this relationship? We'll see in Chapter 3.

Perhaps the most impressive features of the ocean basins are the midoceanic ridges. While not always centered in the oceans as is the Mid-Atlantic Ridge, the three major ocean basins—Atlantic, Pacific, and Indian—all have such a ridge, and the ridges are all connected as well (Figure

1-8). In places the Mid-Atlantic Ridge rises an impressive 3600 meters above the adjacent abyssal plains (Figure 1-9). The ridges are offset by numerous fractures which cross the ridge crests at about right angles. Some of these fractures are essentially cliffs nearly 2 kilometers high, and it is clear that the ridge crests have been displaced along them (Figure 1-8).

Mount Everest, the highest peak on the continents, is 8848 meters (8.8 kilometers) above sea level. The deep ocean floor is on the average 4 kilometers below sea level, and the trenches are as much as 11 kilometers deep. Thus, the earth's surface has a total relief of nearly 20 kilometers. A really rugged surface, isn't it? No, it isn't. We have already mentioned that the earth may appear to us to be flat rather than round, because we are too close to see its curvature. The same thing can be said about the majestic mountains and the other relief on the earth's surface. We are too close to see how unimpressive this ruggedness really is. If the earth were scaled down to the size of an orange and were set beside an orange, the skin of the orange would have much more relief than would the skin of our scaled-down earth. Or put another way, if the earth were scaled to a sphere about 2 meters in diameter, the continents would on the average rise no higher than a thin coat of paint on the model (see Figure 1-10).

Nevertheless, because people are small, let's continue to maintain that earth has some truly impressive topography. How did it all come to be? Did

Figure 1-7 Trenches of the Pacific Ocean and the western Atlantic Ocean. Each is associated with either volcanic island arcs located landward from the trench (such as the Aleutians, the Philippines, and Japan) or volcanic arcs on the adjacent continents (such as the Andes in South America and the volcanoes of Central America).

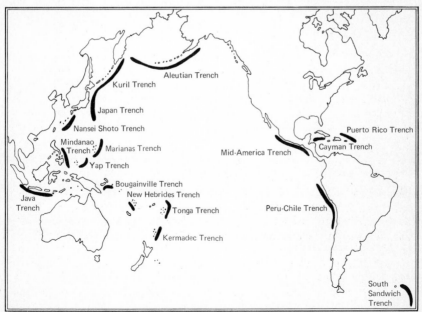

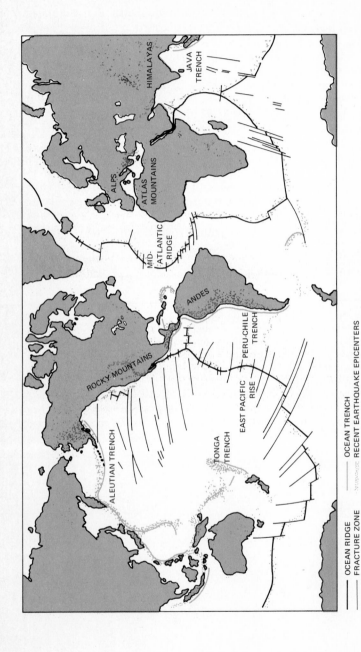

Figure 1-8 Major surface features of the world. Note especially the Mid-Atlantic Ridge and the East Pacific Rise. *(After Konrad B. Krauskopf and Arthur Beiser, 1971, Fundamentals of Physical Science, McGraw-Hill.)*

OCEAN RIDGE ——— ——— OCEAN TRENCH
FRACTURE ZONE ———— RECENT EARTHQUAKE EPICENTERS

ALEUTIAN TRENCH
ROCKY MOUNTAINS
TONGA TRENCH
EAST PACIFIC RISE
PERU-CHILE TRENCH
ANDES
MID-ATLANTIC RIDGE
ALPS
ATLAS MOUNTAINS
HIMALAYAS
JAVA TRENCH

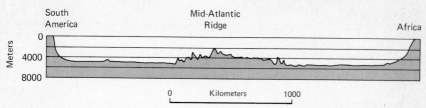

Figure 1-9 Topographic profile of Mid-Atlantic Ridge, midway between South America and Africa. Note great vertical exaggeration. *(After B. C. Heezen, Marie Tharp, and Maurice Ewing, 1959, Geological Society of America Special Paper No. 65.)*

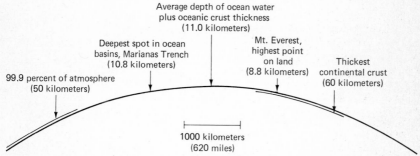

Figure 1-10 Earth's surface and crust drawn approximately to scale. Most features are encompassed within the thickness of a drafted line.

these features all form more or less at random, or is there some overall (underall?) unifying process which can relate and explain all these features? There is such a unifying process which can explain much of the "big picture." But before we can fully appreciate this aspect, we'll have to attain an understanding of the materials of which earth is made. So, on to the next chapter.

TWO

EARTH'S MATERIALS—
THE DETAILED PICTURE

ATOMS

What is matter? All physical things consist of matter, and the fundamental quality of matter is implicit in the origin of the word, from the Latin *mater*, meaning "mother." In the commonplace sense, matter may be described as occupying space (as either a solid, liquid, or gas), as having mass (a measure of quantity), and as having certain physical and chemical properties distinctive to the kind of matter in question.

Early Greeks tried to explain matter. Aristotle about 375 B.C. said all matter is composed of four "elements"—water, fire, air, and earth, distinguished by the qualities of hot, cold, dry, and wet. Furthermore, he said, none are unchangeable; one can become another, with a change in form even though the prime matter in them does not change. For example, rock salt dissolved in water would be a change from earth to water. About the same time another Greek, Democritus, said matter is a concentration of small particles called atoms ("indivisible") which are in constant motion, combine with others, and differ from each other in shape and arrangement. This sounds amazingly like modern atomic theory, but the Aristotelian views prevailed, for Aristotle was a great teacher and a student of much-respected Plato.

In the early 1800s, John Dalton, an English chemist and physicist, proposed the essence of modern atomic theory. He stated that all matter is composed of tiny particles called *atoms* which cannot be changed by chemical changes and that all atoms of a given element weigh the same but differ in weight from atoms of other elements (which is not quite true, as we shall see shortly). We have now found 92 naturally occurring elements on earth, ranging from hydrogen, the lightest, to uranium, the heaviest.

Early in our schooling we learn that atoms are very small—so small in fact, that there can be 100 million per linear inch, or 10^{24} in each 1-inch cube. We have also all learned that atoms are composed of three main smaller particles: positively charged *protons*, negatively charged *electrons*, and neutral *neutrons* (probably consisting of a proton and an electron). The protons and neutrons form the nucleus of an atom, along with more than 30 other kinds of small particles. The electrons move in three-dimensional energy-level shells and subshells around the nucleus at nearly the speed of light. About 99.95 percent of the mass, but only one one-billionth of the volume, of an atom is in the nucleus. Therefore, an atom is mostly space (Figure 2-1). Imagine the sun as the nucleus of an atom; then the atom's diameter would be greater than that of the entire solar system.

In each atom the number of protons is equal to the number of electrons

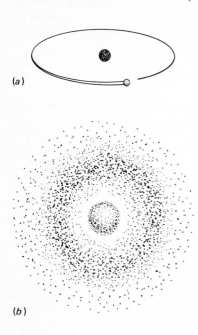
(a)

(b)

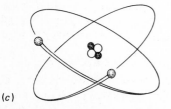
(c)

Figure 2-1 Models of simple atoms. (a) Hydrogen, with its nucleus consisting of only one proton, and with one electron in a three-dimensional spherical orbit around the nucleus. (b) Hydrogen with neither the nucleus nor the electron as a distinct particle. (c) Helium, the next simplest atom, with a nucleus of two protons and two neutrons and two electrons in a single three-dimensional spherical orbit.

and, therefore, each atom is electrically neutral. The number of protons defines the *atomic number* of the element (1 for hydrogen, 92 for uranium), and the number of protons plus neutrons defines the *mass number*, or *atomic weight*, of the element. However, the number of neutrons in atoms of a given element varies. For example, the nuclei of most uranium atoms (with 92 protons) contain 146 neutrons, and hence the mass number is 238 ($^{238}_{92}$U). The nuclei of other uranium atoms contain 143 neutrons, and hence the mass number is 235 ($^{235}_{92}$U). Yet these uranium atoms contain the same number of protons, and their other physical and chemical properties are identical. The atoms of an element which differ in atomic weight are called *isotopes* of that element, and most elements have two or more isotopes. Oxygen has three natural isotopes: ^{16}O (the common one), ^{17}O, and ^{18}O. Hydrogen has three isotopes: ^{1}H (the common one), ^{2}H, and ^{3}H. Carbon has three isotopes: ^{12}C (the common one), ^{13}C, and ^{14}C.

So modern atomic theory has given us the above model of an atom with a nucleus and electrons orbiting it in three-dimensional shells—and let's emphasize that it is a *model*—which fits all the properties of matter which we can measure. The model has changed in the past and will probably change in the future. Today some scientists speak of an "electron mist" rather than discrete negatively charged particles, and others have suggested that protons and neutrons exist not really as distinct particles but as waves or points without volume (Figure 2-1). Another scientist described atoms as "mathematical singularities haunting space." Aren't we back to the original question: What is matter?

There are 92 naturally occurring elements, and 12 more have been created in nuclear reactors. We know that natural radioactive changes take place in some .isotopes, and other elements are the result. Heavier elements change to lighter elements by emitting from the nucleus protons, neutrons, electrons, and short-wavelength energy. For example, $^{238}_{92}$U (uranium) changes, or "decays," to $^{206}_{82}$Pb (lead); this is the principle of atomic fission, or atom splitting. Nuclear fusion, or joining of nuclei, can be illustrated by four hydrogen nuclei (each composed of one proton) joining to make one helium nucleus (two protons and two neutrons).

In both nuclear fission and fusion, the mass of the resultant product is less than the mass of the original material: some mass has been "lost." Einstein has shown us that matter cannot be destroyed but can be changed into energy. That is, energy and mass are two aspects of the same thing. Therefore, no mass is really "lost" in nuclear reactions, but it is instead transformed into energy. Einstein also showed that this energy can be calculated by the formula $E = mc^2$, where m is the transformed mass and c is the speed of light (300,000 kilometers per second, or 186,000 miles per second). Because c is such a large number and is multiplied by itself in the formula, the energy given off in a nuclear reaction is tremendous! This we can verify by recalling the energy of the atom bomb (nuclear fission) and the hydrogen bomb (nuclear fusion).

So we know that new elements are the result of nuclear reactions. Therefore, the logical explanation for the origin of the elements in the first place is by nuclear reactions, probably in dense stars where the temperature is several million degrees Celsius and where neutrons and protons are moving so fast that when they hit each other they fuse together. In such a process, the stars give off immense amounts of energy!

So now it appears that the alchemists of the past weren't completely off base in looking for a method of changing lead into gold. It is at least theoretically possible to make gold out of lead by nuclear reactions. One isotope of lead has 82 protons and 125 neutrons in its nucleus, whereas gold has 79 protons and 118 neutrons. Thus the removal of a few protons and neutrons from the lead nucleus would result in gold.

IONS

The outer energy-level shells of atoms can contain a maximum of eight electrons. The inert gases—neon, krypton, radon, xenon, and argon—have the eight electrons in their outer shells and, hence, are stable and seldom react or join with other atoms to make compounds. All atoms "strive toward stability" by attempting to attain eight electrons in their outer shells. Atoms of sodium and chlorine can be used to illustrate this tendency (Figure 2-2). A sodium atom can most easily have eight electrons in an outer shell by losing the lone electron in its outer shell, thereby making the next shell (with eight electrons) its outer shell. If a chlorine atom, with seven electrons in its outer shell, can add one more electron to that shell, it too has reached the stable configuration. Hence, if a sodium atom loses an electron to a nearby chlorine atom, both are happy.

However, by losing an electron, the sodium atom no longer is a neutral atom with just as many negatively charged electrons as positively charged protons. Instead, it has a net charge of +1, whereas chlorine, after adding an electron, has a net charge of −1. Both have become charged atoms, or *ions.* The positively charged sodium ions and negatively charged chlorine ions combine, or bond together, to form the mineral halite, or common table salt. This bonding of oppositely charged ions is called *ionic bonding.* Why? Because oppositely charged atoms (ions) are attracted to each other by electrostatic forces.

Figure 2-2 Bonding of sodium and chlorine atoms. When a sodium atom gives its outer electron to a chlorine atom, both end up with eight electrons in their outer shells. As neither atom now has as many electrons as protons, both become charged (sodium now has a positive charge and chlorine a negative charge) and are called ions.

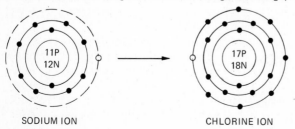

SODIUM ION   CHLORINE ION

Ions have different properties than do their original atoms. Sodium is a very reactive white metal which burns in contact with water and must be stored in oil. Chlorine is a poisonous green gas. But these two ions, when combined, form common table salt, which, of course, is not only harmless but also essential to life. Another example of the difference between a neutral atom and a charged ion is provided by oxygen. Oxygen ions form 94 percent of the volume of the common rocks at the surface of the earth, and yet the oxygen atoms we breathe are certainly quite different chemically than the oxygen in rocks. As has already been intimated, ions are very important as they, rather than electrically neutral atoms, take part in important geological reactions.

The other geologically important type of bonding is *covalent bonding*, in which atoms attain eight electrons in their outer shells by sharing electrons with adjacent atoms, rather than by actually giving up or gaining electrons. The result of such sharing is again charged atoms, or ions. In the sharing of electrons, the ions are bonded together. An example is a water molecule (H_2O): The one electron in the shell of each hydrogen atom, and the six electrons in the outer shell of the oxygen atom, are all shared with each other, thereby in effect giving each of the three atoms eight electrons in its outer shell.

The strength of bonding between ions can vary with the configuration of the ions relative to each other. Graphite and diamond are both formed of pure carbon, yet graphite is one of the softest natural materials and diamond is the hardest.

MINERALS

A *mineral* is a naturally occurring, homogeneous, inorganic crystalline substance with relatively definite chemical and physical properties. *Crystalline* means that the ions are combined in a definite geometric pattern or crystal structure. Figure 2-3 is a model of the halite crystalline structure, showing the fixed positions of the sodium and chlorine ions relative to each other. Chemists speak of the structure of substances in terms of molecules, as they are commonly referring to liquids or gases. However, in the halite

Figure 2-3 Crystal structure of the mineral halite (sodium chloride, or common table salt). The left diagram is an "exploded" model, permitting us to see into the crystal structure. X-ray studies of halite (the first mineral to be studied by x-rays) reveal that the ions are actually touching each other, as in the model to the right.

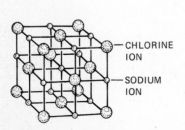

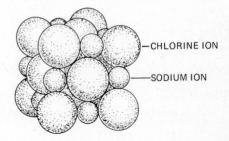

—CHLORINE ION

SODIUM ION

—CHLORINE ION

—SODIUM ION

model, can you say which sodium ion "belongs to" which chlorine ion, thereby making a "halite molecule"? No; each sodium ion is surrounded by six chlorine ions and each chlorine ion by six sodium ions. Each ion is an integral part of the crystal structure. Hence, geologists do not refer to minerals in terms of molecules.

Assuming many different kinds of ions are present, what determines which ions go into making up a given crystal structure? Two of the main factors are *ionic size* and *charge*. Because a crystal structure is a three-dimensional array of ions, with each ion "touching" adjacent ions, the size of the ions is critical. If a given ion is too large, it cannot fit into the structure. Likewise, the electrical charge of an ion, which is determined by the number of electrons gained or lost, is important. Let us look at the buildup of two minerals: olivine and plagioclase. Table 2-1 is a list of a few ions with their charges and ion radii (in Angstroms; 1 Å = 1 × 10^{-8} cm or 0.00000001 cm).

Olivine has the formula $(Fe,Mg)_2 SiO_4$. Since iron and magnesium have similar sizes and charges, they can substitute freely for each other during the crystallization of olivine. Therefore, depending on the abundance of iron and magnesium, the composition of olivine can vary from Fe_2SiO_4 to Mg_2SiO_4; most olivine contains both iron and magnesium. Note that when the electrical charges of the ions are added up, there are an equal number of positive and negative charges. This is a general rule—each crystal must be electrically neutral.

One of the most common minerals in the earth's crust is plagioclase feldspar, which contains variable amounts of sodium and calcium. Sodium plagioclase has the formula $NaAlSi_3O_8$—note that the positive charges balance the negative charges. Because sodium and calcium ions are about the same size, they can substitute for each other. If this happens, will the formula be $CaAlSi_3O_8$? Check the charges; they don't balance. So if calcium subs for sodium, the excess positive charge of the plagioclase must be balanced. This is done in calcium plagioclase by another substitution—an aluminum for silicon—with the final formula being $CaAl_2Si_2O_8$, which is electrically balanced. Most plagioclase contains both sodium and calcium, and therefore some silicons must be replaced by aluminums.

Only 8 of the 92 naturally occurring elements are abundant enough to make up over 1 percent of the earth's crust (Table 2-2).

Furthermore, whereas oxygen makes up 47 percent of the weight of the earth's crust, it also makes up 94 percent of the volume of the earth's crust. In addition, oxygen makes up 89 percent of water by weight and 21 percent of

Table 2-1 Radii and charges of common ions

K^+	= 1.33 Å	(potassium)
Ca^{2+}	= 0.99 Å	(calcium)
Na^{1+}	= 0.97 Å	(sodium)
Si^{4+}	= 0.42 Å	(silicon)
Al^{3+}	= 0.51 Å	(aluminum)
Mg^{2+}	= 0.66 Å	(magnesium)
Fe^{2+}	= 0.74 Å	(iron)
O^{2-}	= 1.32 Å	(oxygen)

Table 2-2 The common elements in earth's crust

ELEMENT	APPROXIMATE ABUNDANCE BY WEIGHT PERCENT
Oxygen (O)	46.6
Silicon (Si)	27.7
Aluminum (Al)	8.1
Iron (Fe)	5.0
Calcium (Ca)	3.6
Sodium (Na)	2.8
Potassium (K)	2.6
Magnesium (Mg)	2.1
	98.5

the atmosphere by weight. Important stuff, that oxygen. Obviously, the elements not listed in Table 2-2 are rare in the earth's crust. For example, copper, which is a metal common to all of us, makes up only 0.000055 percent of the crust by weight.

And just as only a few elements are abundant in the earth's crust, only a few minerals are common; the eight minerals in Table 2-3 make up more than 95 percent of the rocks in the crust. These main rock formers are all *silicates*, minerals made of silicon, oxygen, usually aluminum, and the other positively charged common ions. The basic building block of the silicate minerals is the *silicon-oxygen tetrahedron* of four oxygens with one silicon ion in among them (Figure 2-4). Because oxygens each have a charge of −2 and silicon has a charge of +4, the tetrahedra each have a net charge of −4 and are "complex ions," which act like individual ions. Because of the negative charge, positively charged ions combine with them to form the silicate minerals.

Some tetrahedra are simply held in a mineral structure by positive ions, as in the case of olivine, where iron and magnesium ions bond the structure. In most of the silicates, however, one or more oxygens are shared by adjacent tetrahedra; that is, some oxygen ions are part of two tetrahedra. The tetrahedra thus form chains (as in pyroxene), double chains (as in horn-

Figure 2-4 The silicon-oxygen tetrahedron. Four oxygen ions surround a smaller silicon ion, as shown in the "exploded" model.

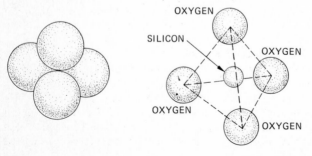

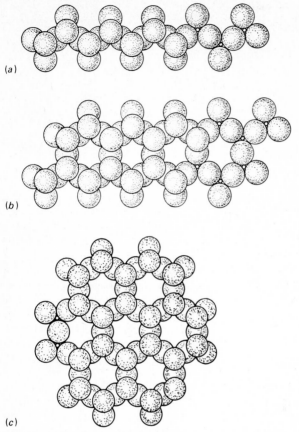

(a)

(b)

(c)

Figure 2-5 Single chains (a), double chains (b), and sheets (c), each illustrating a sharing of oxygens by adjacent tetrahedra. In (a), each tetrahedra shares two oxygens; in (b), some share two and some share three; and in (c), each shares three oxygens. Single chains are joined to other single chains and double chains are joined to other double chains by positively charged ions (such as iron, magnesium, sodium, calcium, and potassium). Similarly, sheets are joined to other sheets by such ions, making stacks of sheets.

blende), and sheets (as in the micas), and where all the oxygens are common to two tetrahedra, three-dimensional structures result as in quartz and the feldspars (Figure 2-5).

Whereas the silicates are volumetrically the most important minerals, there are several other groups of minerals which are economically more valuable. The *oxides* (positive ions plus oxygen) include hematite (Fe_2O_3), limonite ($Fe_2O_3 \cdot H_2O$), and magnetite (Fe_3O_4), the main iron-ore minerals. The *carbonates* (the complex carbonate ion—CO_3—plus positive ions) include calcite ($CaCO_3$), perhaps the most common nonsilicate mineral. The *sulfides* (sulfur plus positive ions) include most of the ores of copper, lead, zinc, and

Table 2-3   The common crust-forming minerals

Muscovite mica	HKAlSiO
Biotite mica	HKFeMgAlSiO
Hornblende	HKNaCaMgFeAlSiO
Pyroxene	CaMgFeAlSiO
Orthoclase feldspar	KAlSiO
Plagioclase feldspar	CaNaAlSiO
Olivine	(Fe, Mg)SiO
Quartz	SiO_2

*For simplicity, formuli are not actual quantitative formuli.

several other metals. The *sulfates* (the complex sulfate ion—SO_4—plus positive ions) include gypsum ($CaSO_4 \cdot 2H_2O$). The *chlorides* (chlorine plus positive ions) include halite (NaCl). A few minerals consist of only one element, such as native gold, silver, copper, and sulfur.

There are more than 2000 known minerals, but as we have already emphasized, only about 10 are volumetrically important and make up any significant part of the rocks of the earth's crust. The eight silicate minerals named in Table 2-3 are all high-temperature minerals and constitute the bulk of igneous and metamorphic rocks. The other main minerals are clay (clay is actually a group of related minerals) and calcite. They are the two most common minerals formed by surface processes and respectively make up shale and limestone, two of the most common sedimentary rocks on earth.

THE ROCK CYCLE

Minerals form under many different conditions, but for each mineral there is a specific range of temperature, pressure, and other conditions under which it is stable. Stated in a different way, minerals are stable only in the environment in which they are formed. For example, olivine forms at depth; it commonly crystallizes from magma under relatively high temperatures and pressures. If olivine is exposed to the temperature, pressure, and humidity of the earth's surface, it is no longer stable and the crystal structure disintegrates. The iron ions combine with oxygen to form iron oxide (hematite), or with oxygen and water to form hydrated iron oxide (limonite). If clay minerals which formed at the earth's surface are deeply buried or subjected to heat and pressure, they change to micas which are stable under the new conditions.

A few minerals, such as quartz, are stable under quite a range of conditions. However, most minerals are not, and since conditions at specific places on the earth's surface commonly change, the minerals change too. Because of crustal movements, minerals which formed at depth are commonly exposed at the earth's surface and minerals formed at the surface are commonly subjected to the conditions at depth. Consequently, change, not stability, is the rule.

Since all rocks are composed of minerals, rocks are only as stable as the minerals of which they are composed. The rocks change too. These changes can be summarized well by means of the *rock cycle* (Figure 2-6). The rock cycle also illustrates that geologic processes result in three main genetic classes of rocks—igneous (those formed from magma), sedimentary (those formed from pieces of other rock material or precipitated out of water), and metamorphic (those formed from other rocks by changes in temperature or pressure and solutions).

The study of these three rock groups is really an exercise in detective work and earth history. Geologists must use every available clue to decipher the events of the past. As James Hall (1811–1891), one of America's great early geologists, said, "The grand problem of geology is the entire history—chemical, physical, zoological and botanical—of the groups of strata (sedimentary layers) constituting the formations of the world." And a thorough study will involve both laboratory work and field work. But are the laboratory and field really different? The field is a geological laboratory in constant operation.

IGNEOUS ROCKS

Most of us are well aware of the fact that molten rock issues forth from volcanoes. We can observe the molten lava (called magma if at depth), and

Figure 2-6 The rock cycle illustrates that changes in its surroundings will cause a rock to change so as to be more stable under the new conditions. Thus, rocks (and obviously, also the minerals which comprise the rocks) are stable only in the environments in which they form. Note that the rock cycle has many shortcuts; rarely does a rock take the circle route. And if it did, wouldn't the only clue to its travels be its chemical composition?

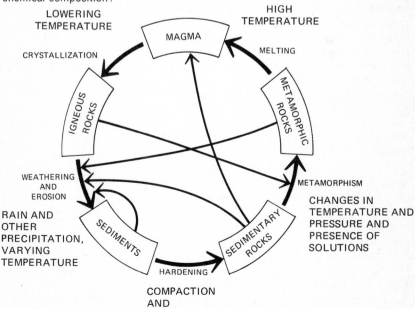

we can see the solid rock which is a result of its crystallization. This type of rock is called igneous rock, from the Latin *igneus*, meaning "of fire." The origin of volcanic rocks seems obvious, although the origin of igneous rocks formed at depth from cooling magma is, of course, less certain.

The volcanic origin of igneous rocks hasn't always been obvious. In the late 1700s, when geology was in its infancy as a science, the leading idea was that the rocks which we now call igneous rocks were precipitated from seawater. Abraham Gottlob Werner of Germany, a dynamic teacher, was the leading proponent of this school of geologic thought, aptly named the *Neptunist* school after Neptune, the Roman god of the sea. Werner was very provincial, and never traveled far from the part of Germany in which he studied and taught; consequently, he had not seen volcanoes in action. (Reportedly he didn't write much, wouldn't even answer letters, and didn't read much either.) When volcanoes were described to him, he cleverly concluded that burning coal beds at depth had melted the rocks which had earlier been precipitated. However, in all fairness, it must be stated that Werner was a great teacher and one of our first good mineralogists. One of his students was William Maclure, one of the first American geologists, who, in 1817, published a book entitled *Observations on the Geology of the United States of America, with Some Remarks on the Effect Produced on the Nature and Fertility of Soils by the Decomposition of the Different Classes of Rocks; and an Application to the Fertility of Every State in the Union in Reference to the Accompanying Geologic Map (with 2 plates).* In spite of the title, the book is very short.

Meanwhile, in Scotland, James Hutton noted stringers of rock which appeared to have resulted from one rock intruding into another, preexisting one. On the basis of a careful study of the rock relationships in the field, he correctly attributed the origin of these stringers to rock once made molten by internal heat. He and his followers were promptly dubbed *Plutonists* after Pluto, the Greek god of the underworld. (Hutton's name will crop up elsewhere in this book in regard to other facets of geology. He is acclaimed the "Father of Geology," a highly deserved title.) Werner had taught the importance of careful field observations. And many of his students could not reconcile what they saw as they traveled widely with what they had been taught. After Werner's death, but not before because of their great respect for him, several of them acknowledged that Werner had been wrong in several instances and that the Plutonists were right.

Magma and Igneous Rock Bodies Magma, or molten rock material, is a solution of oxygen, silicon, aluminum, other ions, water vapor, and other gases. It is very hot, from 500 to 1700°C. Apparently it forms in isolated pockets at relatively shallow depths of a few kilometers to a few tens of kilometers. Because of the behavior of earthquake waves in the earth's crust and mantle, we know that there is no major zone of liquid, from which the magma could emanate. Its derivation must be local, the result of hot spots. The earth's temperature increases with depth, and at a depth of several kilometers the heat is probably enough to cause rocks there to melt.

Likewise, however, the pressures increase with depth and are probably high enough to prevent melting and to keep the ions closely packed in solid crystalline structures in spite of the heat. If this pressure is relieved by cracking along a zone of weakness, the rock could theoretically become liquid. As the pressure is relieved, any water present in the crystalline structures would turn to a gas at the high temperatures and would tend to rise, thereby helping the liquid magma to rise also.

If the magma rises to the surface of the earth, volcanism is the result. (Volcanoes and volcanic rocks are described in the next chapter.) However, much magma does not reach the surface for various reasons: vapor content, composition of the magma, strength of the overlying rock layers, and so on. These magmas cool at depth, and the resultant rocks are exposed only after uplift and erosion have occurred. The rock bodies which formed at depth from crystallization of magma include *batholiths, stocks, sills*, and *dikes* (Figures 2-7 to 2-10). Dikes are the most common, but the large batholiths are the most important.

The Different Igneous Rocks A combination of field and laboratory obserations, plus laboratory experiments with artificial magmas, have yielded much information on the origin of magmas and igneous rocks. One important fact is that the size of the crystals in an igneous rock depends on its rate of cooling. If a magma cools slowly, there is time for the ions with the correct sizes and charges to migrate through the magma to sites on the growing crystal structures, and large crystals result. Conversely, if the magma cools

Figure 2-7 Igneous rock bodies.

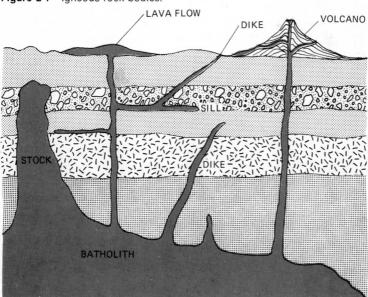

Figure 2-8 Dikes of light-colored granite cutting across metamorphic rock. The dikes cooled at depth but have been exposed by erosion. Note geological hammer for scale.

Figure 2-9 Sills of light-colored granite intruded between and parallel to layers of metamorphic rock.

Figure 2-10 Sierra Nevada batholith, California. View shows part of the 700-kilometer-long and 100-kilometer-wide batholith which intruded into a thick pile of older sedimentary and volcanic rocks and cooled at a depth of many kilometers. Uplifting and erosion of the area (obviously still in progress) have exposed the batholith, which is a complex of many granitic intrusions.

rapidly, there is not time for the ions to travel far, and more numerous, smaller crystals result (Figure 2-11). And, if a magma cools very rapidly, as when lava is extruded into water, there is virtually no time for crystals to grow and the outermost lava cools as a *glass*. (Glass is a supercooled liquid, and over long periods of time it will develop fine crystals.) So the sizes of crystals in igneous rocks reveal much about the history of those rocks and allow most igneous rocks to be classified on the basis of texture as either fine-grained, and hence *volcanic* in origin, or coarse-grained, and hence *plutonic* in origin. That is, magma cooling slowly at depth yields larger crystals than lava cooling at the surface. Of course, some plutonic rocks crystallize relatively fast if the bodies of magma are small, and the edges of a body of magma will cool more quickly and be finer-grained than the better-insulated interior.

In addition to texture, igneous rocks are also classified on the basis of mineralogic and chemical composition (Figure 2-12). Some magmas and igneous rocks are *felsic* (granitic) in composition (high in silicon, potassium, and sodium), and others are *mafic* (basaltic) in composition (high in iron, magnesium, and calcium). These are just the two most common types; there are all gradations between them and even some that are *ultramafic*. With a great variation in the chemical composition of magmas, the resultant igneous rocks will also have a great variety of compositions. Several hundred kinds of igneous rocks have been named. But once again, the number of common rock types is small. Actually, if we define *granite* and *basalt* rather broadly,

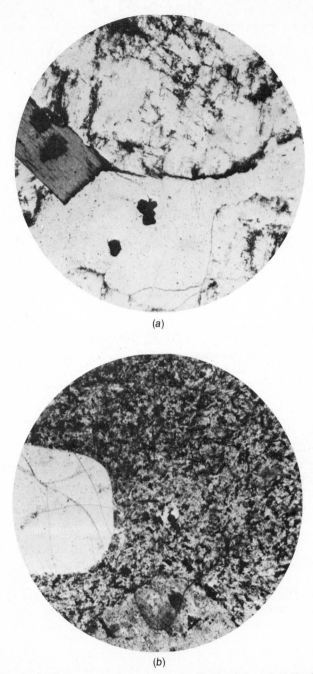

(a)

(b)

Figure 2-11 Photomicrographs of igneous rocks. Fields of view about 2 millimeters in diameter. (*a*) Granite. Note large size of biotite (dark gray), feldspar (light gray with lines), and quartz (clear). (*b*) Rhyolite. Note small size of most crystals of quartz and potassium-feldspar. The large white crystal is quartz and the large gray crystal is potassium-feldspar. Why does this rock have two sizes of crystals? Because the larger crystals formed earlier and grew for a longer time, and the fine crystals cooled rapidly as the magma was extruded at the surface. (*c*) (opposite page) Basalt. Note small size of crystals of plagioclase (elongate white) and mafic (iron-bearing) minerals (dark).

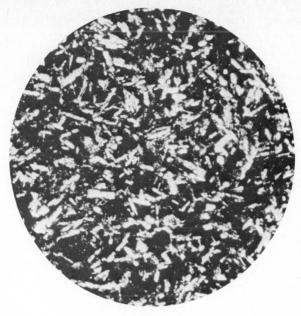

Figure 2-11 continued

(c)

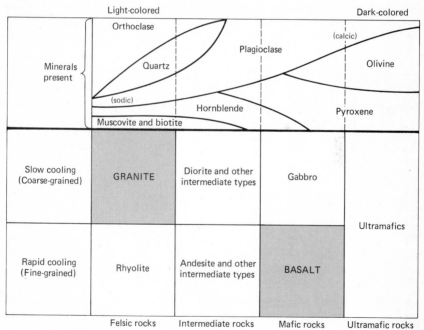

Figure 2-12 Igneous rock chart. The two major igneous rock types, granite and basalt, are shown by bolder print. The other rock types (and hundreds of others could be included) are volumetrically minor. Minerals present in each rock can be determined by reading upward from the rock name. For example, granite can contain muscovite, biotite, hornblende, sodic plagioclase, quartz, and orthoclase, but the essential minerals are orthoclase and quartz, which occupy most of the upper part of the box. On the other extreme, ultramafics contain only pyroxene, olivine, and calcic plagioclase.

these two rock types are the important ones. *Granitic* rocks make up 95 percent of all intrusive rocks, and 95 percent of all extrusive rocks are *basaltic.*

Why Are There Different Kinds of Igneous Rocks?   The obvious answer to this question is that different kinds of magma beget different kinds of igneous rocks. But why are there different kinds of magma? N. L. Bowen of the Geophysical Laboratory in Washington, D.C., suggested in 1922 that most magmas probably start out as basaltic magma. Using both field and laboratory data, Bowen showed that as a basaltic magma cools, the different common igneous minerals form at certain temperatures, with olivine crystallizing first at the highest temperature and quartz crystallizing last at the lowest temperature. The order of crystallization is shown in Figure 2-13. If the early formed olivine crystals remain in the magma, the magma will react with them and will change some olivine to pyroxene. The calcium-rich plagioclase crystals will grow larger, but each successive portion of any crystal will be richer in sodium. And the net result of the crystallization of basaltic magma is, naturally, basalt, a rock largely composed of olivine, pyroxene, and plagioclase (Figure 2-12). However, if the crystals are removed from the magma as they form by settling out of the magma, thereby not reacting with the magma, then the remaining magma will be poorer in iron, magnesium, and calcium. When this remaining magma crystallizes, the minerals formed

Figure 2-13   The order of crystallization of minerals in a basaltic magma as the temperature decreases.

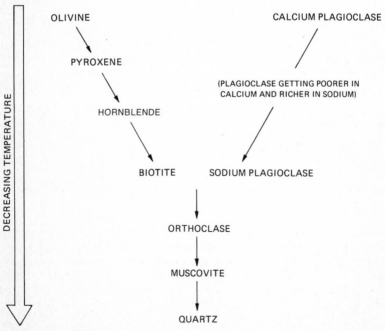

may be hornblende and plagioclase containing both calcium and sodium. And if these crystals are removed from the magma, a different type of rock is the result. The remaining magma is relatively much poorer in iron, magnesium, and calcium and relatively richer in silicon, sodium, and potassium. Again, different rock types, including granite, will result. By this process of removing crystals from the crystallizing basaltic magma, called *fractional crystallization* by Bowen, many different kinds of magmas and rocks can be formed from one original magma.

There is no doubt that Bowen was correct. However, the worldwide importance of this process can be questioned on several grounds. The volume of intermediate rock types is small. Why aren't they more abundant? Granites form the continents and basalts the ocean floors. Why aren't they more closely intermixed if they originated from the same bodies of original magma? And finally, granites should form less than 10 percent of the total if the original magma was basaltic and went through fractional crystallization. Why are they much more abundant, making up the continents?

If fractional crystallization cannot explain all the different types of magmas and igneous rocks, what can? The answer seems to be a simple one. If different types of rocks are melted, different types of magma will result. But how did different rock types form in the first place? The answer to this question is not simple, but must involve all the igneous, sedimentary, and metamorphic process which cause a differentiation, or separation of the elements from a theoretical homogeneous parent material. Differentiation has probably been going on in one way or another since the early days of earth's history.

SEDIMENTARY ROCKS

Sedimentary rock layers today cover about 75 percent of the land surface but make up only about 5 percent of the earth's crust. They thus form only a thin veneer on top of igneous and metamorphic rocks. The igneous or metamorphic rock "basement" beneath the sedimentary layers pokes through this thin cover at numerous places. How this sedimentary cover originated is the topic of this section.

The rock cycle (Figure 2-6) illustrates that rocks which formed at depth under conditions of relatively high temperature and pressure will generally be unstable at the earth's surface, where the temperature averages 20°C, where the pressure is only 1 atmosphere, and where water and air are more abundant. The result is the mechanical and chemical breakdown of rocks by numerous specific processes which are collectively termed *weathering*.

Weathering, Sediment, and Major Sedimentary Rock Types   Weathering results in numerous small fragments collectively called sediment (see Table 2-4) as well as dissolved ions in solution which, when the chemical conditions are proper, will be precipitated out of water as new minerals. Weathering will be discussed again in Chapter 4 at greater length in connection with the formation of soils. At this point, it is sufficient to realize that weathering causes existing rocks to be broken up into smaller pieces (gravel,

Table 2-4 Sizes of sediment

	SIZE, MILLIMETERS
Gravel*	> 2
Sand	$2 - \frac{1}{16}$
Silt	$\frac{1}{16} - \frac{1}{256}$
Clay	$< \frac{1}{256}$

*Includes pebbles, cobbles and boulders. Note that *clay* here is used as a grain size, rather than as a mineral; it has two meanings.

sand, and silt), causes existing minerals to be changed into clay minerals which are stable under the surface conditions, and causes minerals to be dissolved and carried away as ions.

Generalizing a bit, we can state that the three main types of sedimentary rocks and their abundances can be explained in large part by one word— weathering. Shale or mudstone makes up at least 50 percent of all sedimentary rocks (some geologists say 80 percent), sandstone 30 percent, and limestone 20 percent. Actually, there is about 1 percent left over for all the other types of sedimentary rocks, including conglomerate, siltstone, chert, gypsum, salt, coal, and iron formation. Shale and mudstone are made up mainly of clay minerals and fine silt particles which were formed during weathering. Sandstones include grains of quartz (which is very resistant to weathering) and other minerals, and rock fragments which are not yet completely weathered. Limestones are made up of the mineral calcite ($CaCO_3$), the result of the combination of calcium ions (provided by weathering) and carbon dioxide in seawater.

Loose sediment is transformed or lithified into hard sedimentary rock in several ways. Clay particles in shale and mudstone are mainly just squeezed together, or compacted, thereby reducing the amount of open space, or pores, between grains. Sand grains and pebbles require cementation, generally by silica or calcite which is precipitated out of groundwater moving through the sediment. Calcite grains are commonly cemented together by calcite, and minor recrystallization of calcite grains is also common. Clay can also serve to bind sand grains together.

Movement and Deposition of Sediment—Principles The sediment provided by weathering does not usually stay where it was formed. If any slope is present, the sediment will generally be carried off by moving (running) water (or under special conditions by wind or glacial ice) and deposited elsewhere as a layer or bed of sediment. These processes of erosion, transportation, and deposition are common sights on a local scale during any good rainfall. The speed of the running water, plus several other factors, commonly results in a size sorting of the sediment. Hence, the larger grains may be deposited where the current first slows appreciably, the sand-sized grains may be dropped further downcurrent where the velocity has decreased still more, and finally, the smaller silt and clay-sized particles will be deposited where the current has practically stopped. We can observe streams and beaches and see that sediment is deposited when the velocity of the moving water decreases. Thus, we can expect large deposits of sediments at the bases of mountains where streams suddenly slow down and in lakes or oceans where rivers enter them and their velocity is checked.

Similarly, close observation will reveal the constant sorting action of moving water or sediments. Observations of hard sedimentary rock layers show that they are also commonly size-sorted and that there are beds composed of pebbles (conglomerate), others of sand (sandstone), others of silt (siltstone), and still others of clay and silt (shale and mudstone). By analogy with modern observable processes, doesn't it seem logical that these sedimentary rock layers were formed by the same processes which are affecting loose sediment today? Indeed, it has seemed logical to all geologists since the days of James Hutton, who in 1795 published *The Theory of the Earth*, the first geology textbook. Unfortunately, Hutton wrote in a correct but very hard-to-read style. Fortunately, one of his good friends, John Playfair, a mathematician at Edinburgh, where Hutton taught, clarified Hutton's ideas in *Illustration of the Huttonian Theory of the Earth*, which was published in 1802. After 30 years of observation of natural processes at work in the field, Hutton had formulated the *principle of uniformitarianism*, which can be simply stated as "the present is the key to the past." That is, by observing present processes at work and seeing the products of these processes, we can better understand older rocks and their origins. This is now an underlying principle in practically all geological investigations. Hutton did *not* specify that processes at work today are proceeding at the same rate as in the past. Change is the name of the game, and the rates at which processes proceed may change drastically from time to time.

Good observation will also reveal that layers of sediment are generally deposited in a nearly horizontal position; this is another basic geologic principle, the *principle of original horizontality*. Assuming this principle is a correct one, then if sedimentary rock layers are inclined at a steep angle, they have obviously been moved into that position by earth disturbances sometime after their deposition.

Another observation that may seem absurdly simple to us is that in a given pile of undisturbed, horizontal rock layers (as in Figure 2-14), the youngest layer is at the top and the oldest at the bottom. However, this realization, now called the *law of superposition*, by Nicholas Steno (a Dane) in 1669, was a giant step forward in interpreting earth history. Prior to this, virtually everyone believed in an instant creation of the earth and its inhabitants and, therefore, assumed that all rocks were the same age. Likewise, to those who adhered to the idea of instantaneous creation, the principles of uniformitarianism and original horizontality were completely irrelevant as well as irreverent.

The acceptance of these three principles—uniformitarianism, original horizontality, and superposition—as basic principles to be utilized in the study of sedimentary rocks was therefore an essential beginning both to the understanding of the origins of sedimentary rocks and to the deciphering of the earth's history.

Figure 2-14 Grand Canyon, Arizona. The sedimentary rock layers were deposited as horizontal layers over a vast expanse of geologic time. In more recent geologic times (within the last 10 million years) the area has been uplifted and erosion by the Colorado River has exposed the many pages of earth history. Resistant rock types, sandstones and limestones, form cliffs, whereas the softer shales form the gentler slopes. *(Courtesy of C. L. Matsch.)*

   The ultimate resting place of most sediment is the sea, for running water always moves downhill toward the sea, carrying the sediment with it. However, the journey for a sand grain from a mountain top to the sea may be a long one, comprised of many short jaunts and long stops at places along the way. Most of the sedimentary rocks shown in Figure 2-14 were deposited in the sea, as evidenced by their marine fossils. Therefore, the seas must have covered these parts of the continent in the past. In fact, the seas have advanced onto and retreated from the continents many times in the past. Why? Obviously either sea level rose or the continents sank. The transgressions of the seas onto the landmasses could theoretically be caused by an increase in the amount of water in the oceans. However, there is only so much water on earth, and only minor variations in the amount of water in the oceans are thought to have occurred in the past. Theoretically, if enough sediment was carried into the oceans by rivers, sea level would go up, just as the water level in your bathtub rises when you enter it. However, any appreciable rises in sea level would require fantastically large volumes of sediment to be dumped into the ocean. Another possible explanation is a raising of the sea floor; again, a great amount of uplift over a large part of the ocean floor would be necessary. Or, seas could have advanced onto the continents because of downward movements of the continents and have withdrawn as the continents moved upward. The answer seems to lie in one of the last two possibilities, vertical movements of the continents or of the ocean basins.

This sedimentary cover over most of the continents is from 0 to 3 kilometers thick. In certain regions on every continent, however, the sedimentary layers have a total thickness of as much as 15 kilometers! One might logically ask whether the deposition of such thicknesses doesn't require great earth catastrophes, in direct opposition to the principle of uniformitarianism?

One example of a thick pile of sedimentary rocks is along the west side of the Great Valley of California. Here the base of a 10,000-meter-thick tilted sequence is known by fossil and radiometric age dates to be about 130 million years old, whereas beds high in the sequence are 80 million years old (Figure 2-15). Hence, it took 50 million years for the pile to accumulate. Some

Figure 2-15 Portion of 10,000-meter-thick pile of sedimentary rocks on west side of Sacramento Valley (north part of the Great Valley), California. The light-colored beds are sandstones and the dark colored ones are mainly mudstones. Mountain building caused the sequence to be uplifted, tilted, and eroded.

(a)

(b)

Figure 2-16 Cross-bedding. (a) Unconsolidated pebbly sands deposited by a river about 10,000 years ago. (b) Slightly tilted, hard sandstone beds deposited about half a billion years ago. In each case, the currents that deposited the sands were generally moving from left to right.

simple arithmetic shows this to be an average annual accumulation of only 0.2 millimeters per year, a rate comparable to modern sedimentation in the ocean relatively near continents. Therefore, we have another important principle—"much time is available"—to accompany uniformitarianism, original horizontality, and superposition as basic geologic tenets.

Movement and Deposition of Sediment—Evidence   We've stated that most sedimentary rocks deposited upon the continents in the geological past are marine. And today as well, the ultimate resting place for most sediment is the ocean. Rivers are continually transporting sediment, as well as dissolved ions, from the continents to the sea. What happens to it there?

Some of the sediment stays on the continental shelves, there to be moved about and reworked time and time again by waves and currents in the relatively shallow waters. A prominent feature of sand-sized sediment deposited in such shallow-water environments by currents is medium-scale cross-bedding (Figure 2-16). By measuring the direction that cross-beds in a rock layer dip, the "paleocurrent" or old current direction, can be determined. This can then be used to help determine the *paleogeography* at the time of deposition. Ripple marks (Figure 2-17) which are asymmetrical also give the current direction; symmetrical ones are attributed to wave action.

Because the fossils found in a large portion of the sedimentary rocks upon the continents are of organisms that lived in shallow seas, a common statement in textbooks of a few decades ago was that there probably are few, if any, deep-water sediments now exposed as sedimentary rock upon the continents, implying among other things that little sediment is transported seaward beyond the shelves. More detailed studies in the past few decades both of the sedimentary rock column on land and of the ocean floor have revealed that much sediment is carried off the shelf into deeper water and deposited on the continental slope and at the base of the slope. The layers in

Figure 2-17   Ripple marks exposed on beds which have been tilted and eroded.

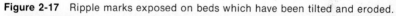

Figure 2-15, for example, may have had such an origin. Great subsea fans and sediment wedges exist at the bases of the continental slopes around most continents (Figure 2-18). These sediments have literally buried irregular terrains, including numerous dead volcanoes, and must be very thick. For example, by reflecting sound waves off different sediment layers within these fans, geophysicists have found that the sediment wedge off the Eastern United States is as much as several thousand meters thick.

How is the sediment moved down the continental slopes? Underwater sand flow down the steep gradient of LaJolla Canyon, off California, has been observed by diving oceanographers. Some scientists feel that such sand flow is a very important mechanism of transport. However, such a sand flow probably cannot account for *graded beds*, beds of silty or sandy material which display a general decrease in average grain size from the bottom to the top of the bed (Figure 2-19). Such beds are often somewhat clayey throughout, indicating fairly poor sorting, and are called "dirty" beds. These graded beds are most common in sedimentary rock units which have recently been interpreted as fan deposits. In many places thousands of beds show such grading.

The most commonly accepted origin for abundant dirty graded beds is deposition by turbidity currents. A *turbidity current* is a dense, muddy, turbulent current which moves down slopes at great speed because of its greater density compared with the surrounding seawater. When such a

Figure 2-18 Deep-sea fans at base of continental slope off California. Vertical exaggeration is approximately 20 times. *(From H. W. Menard, Jr., 1960, courtesy of Geological Society of America Bulletin.)*

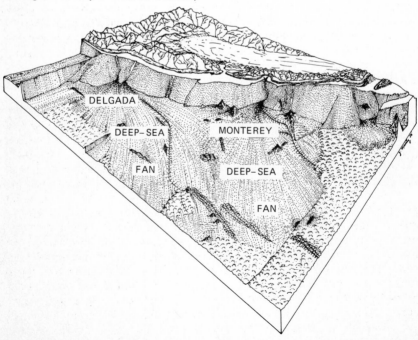

Figure 2-19 Graded sandstone beds between beds of mudstone. Note the coarse bottoms and fine-grained tops; the sharp bottom contacts and the less obvious top contacts emphasize the grading.

current slows down at or near the base of the slopes, the largest and heaviest grains carried by the current settle first and the lightest settle last, resulting in the grading. As the entire turbulent current, which could presumably be tens of meters thick, carries mud, the resultant graded bed may be somewhat muddy throughout its thickness. By contrast, explosive volcanic debris settling through a thick column of water will form a "clean" graded bed, as every grain must fall through the entire thickness of water, and all the clay-sized particles will settle last.

   Although turbidity currents have been produced in the laboratory, we should still speak of turbidity current *theory*, for no one has actually *seen* a turbidity current on the ocean floor. One of the best cited examples presumably occurred off the Grand Banks of Newfoundland in 1929. An earthquake there apparently triggered a submarine landslide which moved downslope, incorporating water and developing into a turbidity current. This current moved up to about 100 kilometers per hour, severing in sequence numerous transatlantic submarine cables (Figure 2-20). Whether a turbidity current actually caused these cables to break has been a subject for much argument among geologists. In the 1950s the argument was solved at least to the satisfaction of pro-turbidity-current scientists. In an oceanographic expedition, two core samples were obtained from the area in which the turbidity current presumably had stopped. P. H. Kuenen had predicted a graded layer 40 to 100 centimeters thick would be found in the area. The bed at these two spots was, indeed, graded and was 70 and 130 centimeters thick.

   Why doesn't someone sit down on the ocean floor in a bathysphere and

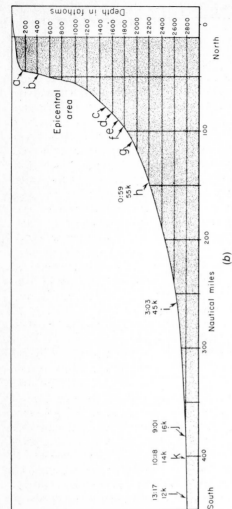

Figure 2-20 Map and cross section of area of Grand Banks earthquake and turbidity current of November 18, 1929. Newfoundland is shown in black and the shallow banks are shown in gray. A submarine landslide originated at point X as a result of the earthquake, and it became a turbidity current as it picked up water in its movement downslope. The lines crossing the area are trans-atlantic cables. Dots 1 through 7 indicate coring stations. The numbers above points h through l (diagram *b*) show the times at which the cable there snapped and the calculated speed of the turbidity current in knots (1 knot = 1 nautical mile per hour) as it passed. *(After B. C. Heezen, and Maurice Ewing, 1952; B. C. Heezen, D. B. Ericson, and Maurice Ewing, 1954; and C. O. Dunbar, and John Rodgers, Principles of Stratigraphy, Wiley, 1957.)*

wait for a turbidity current? Because he might have to wait quite a while. Recall the 10,000-meter-thick sequence in California mentioned earlier in this chapter. The sequence is made up almost completely of alternating beds of mudstone and graded sandstone (Figures 2-15 and 2-19). Of the 10,000-meter total, about one-third consists of the graded sandstone beds. If we assume a turbidity-current origin for the graded beds, then each bed was the result of a very rapid event of a few minutes or hours and, geologically speaking, took virtually no time to occur. Therefore, deposition of the remaining 6700 meters of mudstone must have occupied the 50-million-year time span in which the sequence accumulated. The depositional rate for the mud is, therefore, about 0.134 millimeters per year, or about 13.4 centimeters per 1000 years. (This is much higher than the rate of mud accumulation today in the deeper parts of the modern oceans, where the rate is commonly less than 1 millimeter per 1000 years. It is comparable, however, to the accumulation rates of mud relatively near the continents, as off the coast of Southern California, where rates are 11 to 21 centimeters per 1000 years.) The mudstone layers between the graded sandstones commonly vary from about 5 centimeters to 30 meters in thickness. Who would want to sit in a bathysphere and wait possibly a few hundred years for the next turbidity current?

We have discussed and illustrated two main types of beds: cross-beds and graded beds. Another type is also common, a *massive bed* with no obvious internal structure (Figure 2-21). Such beds can vary in thickness from a few centimeters to many meters. The origin of massive beds is a bit harder to figure out. Did they form by slow and steady deposition of sediment or are they a result of a rapid dumping of sediment without time for reworking? Probably both processes have occurred. However, geologists have x-rayed slabs of massive sandstones and found that some do contain cross-beds and other structures which just are not visible to the naked eye. Paper-thin layers of clay minerals are recorded on the x-ray photos, revealing the structures. (How would you like to go to the University Health Service with a slab of sandstone and talk the staff into x-raying it?)

Thinly laminated beds, a fourth type (Figure 2-22), are relatively simple to interpret, at least in a gross sense. They are composed of clay and silt, and the fine bedding indicates deposition by weak currents or a gentle raining down of material from above. The undisturbed nature of the beds indicates a protected environment of deposition, such as a protected bay or deep water. In any case, deposition was beneath the level where waves were able to rework the bottom material. Laminated beds also indicate a lack of bottom-dwelling organisms, which commonly ingest the fine sediment, take out the food, and then excrete the remainder. It has been said that the sediment on the floor of the Gulf of Mexico, for example, has been completely ingested several times over. Obviously, such appetites would disturb the bedding.

Some Important Sedimentary Rock Types The sand grains themselves also provide clues to a history of long transportation and reworking (abrasion) by waves and currents, displaying a higher degree of roundness and better size-sorting than do less reworked sands such as those deposited

Figure 2-21 Massive beds of sandstone in northeastern Utah near Dinosaur National Monument. These were deposited by ancient rivers.

Figure 2-22 Thinly laminated beds of siltstone deposited in quiet water.

in rivers. And the composition of the grains is also affected. Only the grains composed of the chemically and mechanically durable minerals survive long abrasion. Quartz is the most durable common mineral, so a quartz sandstone may indicate a long, rough history. The grains have been dragged, bounced, attacked with chemicals, and just generally beat up. Only the toughest survive. In fact, geologists think that a well-rounded, well-sorted *quartz sandstone* must have had a history involving several different cycles of uplift, erosion, and abrasion (Figure 2-23*a*). Roundness does not always imply a long history. Pebbles can be rounded by only a few miles of river transport because with their greater mass they hit each other with a greater impact, which causes chipping off of corners and hence rounding. However, experiments by P. H. Kuenen of the Netherlands indicate that more than a million kilometers of river transport is necessary to make quartz sand grains well rounded, for the water cushions grains against impact by other grains. Swashing back and forth on a beach probably does it faster, and wind-propelled grains hitting each other can become rounded relatively quickly because air does not provide the cushion which water does.

Another major type of sandstone, *arkose*, contains abundant angular feldspar grains as well as quartz and, therefore, indicates a history of less weathering, transport, and abrasion (Figure 2-23*b*). A third type of sandstone, *graywacke*, is a dark gray to green, poorly sorted, angular, clayey sandstone comprised of a variety of sand-sized minerals and rock fragments (Figure 2-23*c*). The poor sorting, emphasized by the abundance of clay mixed with sand, is the result of very little reworking. Graywackes are, in fact, "dumped" sandstones, and many may be turbidity-current deposits. One geologist has compared graywackes to a city dump, for they can contain virtually anything. By contrast, he compared quartz sandstones to a well-washed city street.

The mudstones, shales, siltstones, sandstones, and conglomerates we have mentioned so far are the result of the transport of sediment *into* the basin of deposition from *outside* the basin of deposition. The main type of sedimentary rock which originates *within* the basin of deposition is *limestone*, made up of the mineral calcite. Calcium ions are also originally carried *into* the basin in solution as calcium bicarbonate, $Ca(HCO_3)_2$, but then may be precipitated as calcite, $CaCO_3$, as follows:

$$Ca(HCO_3)_2 \rightleftharpoons CaCO_3 + H_2O + CO_2$$

Any process which takes CO_2 out of the seawater, such as the photosynthesis of marine plants, will cause the above reaction to move toward the right if the water is saturated with respect to calcium bicarbonate (and warm seawater

Figure 2-23 Photomicrographs of sandstones. Fields of view about 2 millimeters in diameter. (a) Quartz sandstone. The gray material between grains is calcite cement. Note well-rounded grains, the result of long abrasion. (b) (opposite page) Arkose sandstone. Quartz grains are light gray. Orthoclase and plagioclase grains are darker gray, have parallel lines within the grains (cleavage, the manifestation of the crystalline pattern of planes of ions), and are darker gray because of fine clay minerals which are the result of alteration. Note angularity of grains. The cement between the grains is hard to distinguish. (c) (opposite page) Graywacke sandstone. Quartz grains are light gray, feldspar grains are a darker gray, and various rock fragments are dark gray to black. Note that the angular grains are held together by gray material (clay) between the grains.

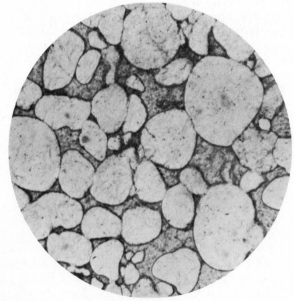

(a)

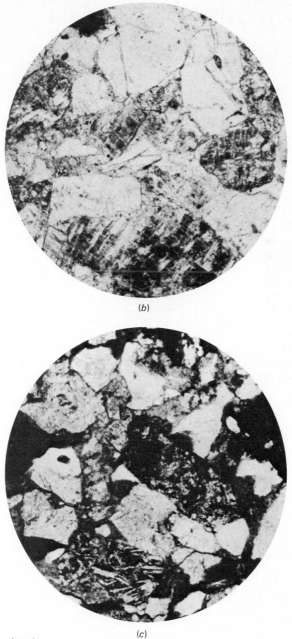

(b)

(c)

Figure 2-23 continued

commonly is), thereby forming calcite as a precipitate. And many sea animals take calcite out of the water to form their shells. Many limestones are made up largely of broken or whole pieces of shells; even fine-grained limestones (such as chalks) contain an abundance of microscopic shells (Figure 2-24).

(a)

(b)

Figure 2-24 Limestones. (a) View of the White Cliffs of Dover, composed of fine-grained limestone (chalk). (b) Microscopic view of the chalk; note the very fine grains and the small fossil shells, which are a fraction of a millimeter in diameter. (The field of view is about 2 millimeters in diameter.) (c) (opposite page) Closeup of a limestone outcrop in Utah; note the shells in certain layers and the differences in grain size of the different layers. (d) (opposite page) Microscopic view of a limestone such as that pictured in c. Note the shells which are cemented by calcite; view is about 2 millimeters in diameter.

(c)

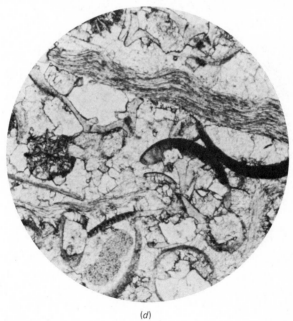

(d)

Figure 2-24 continued

Therefore, it appears that nearly all limestones owe their existence, at least in part, to organisms. As further evidence of this, limestones are uncommon in the rock record before plants and animals became relatively abundant in the seas.

Many limestones have undergone alteration after deposition; magnesium ions from seawater replace part of the calcium ions of the calcite, resulting in the mineral *dolomite*—$CaMg(CO_3)_2$—and the rock *dolostone*. Dolostone is commonly buff-colored. It contains many holes, or cavities, evidently the result of the recrystallization of calcite to denser dolomite. Limestone also commonly contains lenses and nodules of *chert*, which is fine-grained SiO_2. The SiO_2 replaces the $CaCO_3$, and even fossils in the limestone can be completely replaced. Chert also occurs as thin beds, evidently the result of precipitation from seawater.

The Lateral Extent of Sedimentary Beds   If we were studying a sedimentary bed in the field and noted outcrops of identical-appearing rock at many localities tens to hundreds of kilometers apart, we might intuitively think that the sedimentary bed just continued on and on without change. And likewise for the beds above and beneath this bed. This is the "layer-cake" concept of geology, and it has led many early (and present?) geologists to go astray. Some beds do indeed have a wide extent, depending upon the depositional conditions, but a close study of any bed or unit of sediment or sedimentary rock will generally reveal a lateral change in the type of sediment within that unit. These lateral changes are called *sedimentary facies* of that unit (Figure 2-25). They can be observed along nearly any modern shoreline. It may be muddy at one place, sandy at another, and pebbly elsewhere. As we should expect, study of sedimentary rocks in the field shows that sedimentary facies are common in the ancient rock record as well.

An example of simple-appearing geology that is in reality complex is provided by the St. Peter Sandstone, a marine quartz sandstone about 475 million years old. The St. Peter is generally less than 60 meters thick but extends from Minnesota to Missouri and from Illinois to Kansas. It may seem obvious that there was a shallow sea existing over this area 475 million years ago with its bottom covered by quartz sand. But this was probably never the case. The sand at any given time was probably deposited in shallow water near the shore of the sea; farther out to sea mud was probably being deposited, and where no mud and sand could be carried, limestone was being formed. So if you had been able to study that sea floor, you would have found different sediments at different places: sedimentary facies. However, as the sea level rose and the initial "St. Peter Sea" continued to advance northward onto the continent, the successive sandy shore zones merged into each other, forming a continuous sandy layer. And then, wouldn't the southern parts of the St. Peter be older than the northern parts?

Summary Statement on Sedimentary Rocks   The study of sedimentary rocks can be especially fascinating, as so much history can be reconstructed by a patient analysis. Not only can a detailed study of sedimentary features and mineralogy show quite specifically the areas from whence the sedimen-

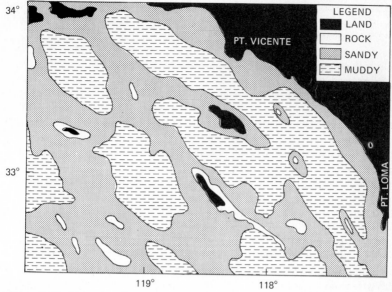

Figure 2-25 Map of sedimentary facies on sea floor off coast of Southern California. Note that the sands are deposited near land or near rock outcrops on the sea floor. *(After Roger Revelle and F. P. Shepard, 1939, in Recent Marine Sediments, American Association of Petroleum Geologists.)*

tary grains were derived, but also it can reveal much about what has happened to the sediment since it was initially eroded. A thorough investigation of a sandstone unit may never hold the same appeal to most people as would one of Arthur Conan Doyle's Sherlock Holmes mysteries, but nevertheless, it does fascinate some geologists.

METAMORPHIC ROCKS

Metamorphism means a change in form: metamorphic rocks have undergone changes in texture or mineralogy or both. If rocks are subjected to pressures and temperatures which differ considerably from those under which they were formed, the minerals in the rocks may change to new minerals which are stable under those new conditions (Figure 2-6). Or, the existing minerals may simply recrystallize into larger crystals. Metamorphism of rocks occurs beneath the surface of the earth, generally at depths of many thousand meters. The boundary between true metamorphic changes and those changes which are considered part of the sedimentational processes, such as cementation or compaction of sediments, is gradational.

What Causes Metamorphism? The change in conditions can be a result of an actual movement of the rocks to a different environment. For example, when a portion of the crust subsides and sedimentary rocks are buried beneath other sedimentary rocks, then the pressure and temperature will be higher. Or the pressure and temperature may change without the rocks actually moving from their site of formation, for example, when a hot magma invades an area. It may seem from what has been said so far that increased pressure and temperature are the causes of metamorphism, but changes to lower pressures and temperatures also cause metamorphism. For example, basalt crystallizes at temperatures of about 1000°C; when basalt, composed largely of plagioclase and pyroxene, is held at temperatures of 300 to 400°C, new minerals form and the rock becomes a *greenstone*, a rock rich in chlorite or hornblende.

The boundary between high-grade metamorphism and igneous process-es is also gradational and occurs at high pressures and at temperatures of about 650°C, which is the lowest temperature at which granitic magma can form.

A rock undergoing metamorphism may simply recrystallize into a coarser-grained rock of larger crystals, with no changes in mineral or chemical composition. This is commonly the case when limestone is meta-morphosed into *marble*; both are composed of the mineral calcite (Figure 2-26*d*). And quartz sandstone may be recrystallized into a harder rock named *quartzite*. Or new minerals may be formed without any actual change in the overall chemistry of the rock. For example, a shale composed largely of clay minerals may be changed to a *slate,* which consists of microscopic mica grains, or to a *schist,* in which the micas are large and visible to the eye (Figure 2-26*a, b,* and *c*). However, if hot watery solutions are present during metamorphism, then ions are readily transported from one place to another and actual changes in the amounts of the various ions present may result. Such waters commonly bring in new ions and carry away some ions which were originally present. Many *gneisses*, which are coarsely banded rocks, have had potassium added to their original composition.

What minerals commonly make up metamorphic rocks? Many minor minerals are characteristic of metamorphic rocks only; staurolite, kyanite, sillimanite, andalusite, talc, and asbestos are some of them. Garnet is commonly metamorphic (Figure 2-27) but does occur in some igneous rocks as well. However, the same eight minerals which you have learned as the common igneous minerals are volumetrically the important metamorphic minerals. And why not, for aren't they all relatively high-temperature miner-als?

Whereas volcanic or sedimentary rocks form at the earth's surface and are relatively easy to study by applying the principle of uniformitarianism, plutonic rocks and metamorphic rocks cannot be studied by observing modern examples in the process of formation. Consequently, plutonic and metamorphic rocks are studied in the field *after* they have been uplifted and exposed by erosion of the rock cover under which they formed. This field study of metamorphic rocks, when coupled with laboratory study, yields much information on mineral stability.

Laboratory containers ("bombs") are loaded with chemicals or minerals of certain compositions and then subjected to various temperatures, pres-sures, and solutions. The conditions expected at depths of as much as 30 kilometers can be simulated. However, one factor cannot be reproduced in the laboratory—the long time spans, up to millions of years, over which certain conditions probably prevail in nature. So scientists run most experiments for only a few days or up to a month and hope that any significant changes will have occurred in that period. Therefore, when a certain assemblage of minerals is found in a metamorphic rock, geologists have a pretty good idea of the conditions under which that metamorphic rock formed.

Fortunately, many minerals in rocks have been "caught in the act" of changing to other minerals when the pressures and temperatures changed before the mineralogical changes were completed. These can be studied in detail under a microscope (Figure 2-28).

Types of Metamorphism In Scotland, G. Barrow traced unmetamorphosed shales through a series of gradual metamorphic changes and finally into a high-grade metamorphosed rock (Figure 2-29). The clay of the shale was gradually changed to chlorite, biotite, staurolite, garnet, kyanite, and sillimanite, in that order, from the area of low temperatures and pressures toward the area of higher temperatures and pressures. The same sequence was found in other parts of the world, and the system of *metamorphic grade* was developed, with certain minerals signifying that particular temperature and pressure boundaries had been passed.

After detailed work by several geologists in Scandinavia and Finland, and especially by Pentti Eskola of Finland, the concept of *metamorphic facies* was established. It is similar to the system of metamorphic grade, but it utilizes groups of minerals rather than individual minerals to define a facies, and hence certain ranges of pressure and temperature. Furthermore, it can be applied as well to metamorphosed basaltic rocks, in which many of the marker minerals found in metamorphosed shales will not form because of the different chemical composition of basalts. Most metamorphic rocks can be placed into one of a half-dozen main metamorphic facies.

If the pressure during metamorphism is about equal in all directions, the resulting metamorphic rock will have an equigranular texture, as is common in many marbles (Figure 2-26d). On the other hand, if the pressure during metamorphism is markedly stronger in a certain direction, any recrystallized old minerals and any new minerals will be aligned parallel to each other in planes and the rock will assume a *foliation*, as illustrated in Figures 2-26b and c. Some foliation may be controlled by the original bedding or layering in the rock, but most is completely due to metamorphism.

Broadly speaking, metamorphism can be classified as either contact or regional, based on the scale of the metamorphism. *Contact metamorphism* is found adjacent to igneous rock bodies, the result of the increased temperature from the magma (Figure 2-30). In effect, the "country rock" into which the magma intruded is baked by the heat. Contact metamorphism is found in narrow zones around intrusions, but naturally a big intrusion, such as a batholith, may have a zone of contact metamorphism as much as several kilometers wide. In contrast to contact metamorphism is *regional metamorphism*, which, as the name implies, occurs over broad areas. Regionally

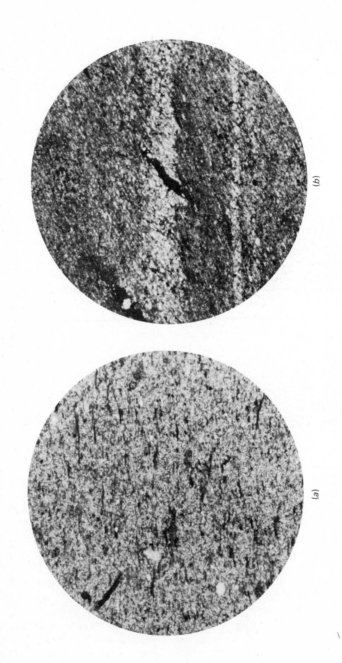

(b)

(a)

(c)

(d)

Figure 2-26 Photomicrographs of metamorphic rocks. (a), (b), and (c) illustrate the development of slate and schist from shale, and (d) illustrates marble. Fields of view are about 2 millimeters in diameter. (a) Shale. Note small subparallel flakes of clay minerals and minor silt grains in this unmetamorphosed sedimentary rock. (b) Slate. Note original silty beds (light gray bands) which were present in the original shale and countless very fine parallel planes cutting across beds. These planes exist because of fine mica flakes which grew from the clay minerals. Black portions are organic matter. (c) Biotite schist. Dark parallel grains are biotite; the white portions consist of composites of quartz grains. The rock had an origin similar to the slate, but the pressure and temperature were more intense or lasted longer, resulting in larger crystals. (d) Marble which formed from limestones such as illustrated in Figure 2-24d. Mineral composition is completely calcite, as in limestone; dark areas are calcite crystals in different optical orientations.

Figure 2-27 Garnet crystals which grew in an impure limestone during metamorphism; some silicon may have been added by solutions. Pencil for scale.

Figure 2-28 A garnet crystal in a chlorite-rich rock. The garnet is the light parts of the crystal and biotite and chlorite are shades of gray and black. Both the garnet and the chlorite formed by metamorphism from a mafic igneous rock. The garnet crystal was subsequently replaced by biotite and chlorite in another metamorphic event, but the replacement was not completed. Therefore, we can see original garnet laced by later biotite and chlorite. Field of view is about 2 millimeters in diameter.

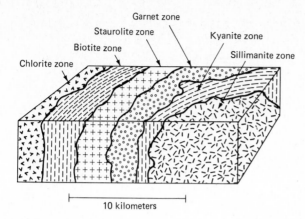

Figure 2-29 Diagrammatic representation of metamorphic zones proceeding from the low-metamorphism zone (chlorite) to the high-metamorphism zone (sillimanite). The mineral assemblages in each zone differ, but each zone has the same chemical composition.

metamorphosed rocks are generally highly folded and broken, indicating the prevalence of directional pressures, and are usually accompanied by large granite batholiths as well. Well-foliated mica-rich rocks (schists) and well-banded rocks (gneisses) are common in such areas. Presumably the happy home of such rocks is in the interiors of mountain ranges, and long-continued erosion of the mountains has exposed them.

Metamorphic Granites?   Some geologists assume that the granitic batholiths in regionally metamorphosed terrains supplied the heat for metamorphism and, in effect, were a partial *cause* of the metamorphism. Others say that the granites are not the cause but the *effect* of metamorphism. The latter are thus saying that not all granites are igneous (heresy!), but that some have formed from the transfer of ions by hot waters into preexisting rocks, thereby transforming, or *granitizing*, them. Presumably it should be relatively easy to tell, but it isn't. Geologists in the late 1930s argued the "granite problem" with great vigor and vehemence. The magmatists called the granitizers "soaks." The granitizers called the magmatists "pontificators," probably because they acted as if crystallization from magma were a holy process, not to be doubted. One famous geologist exclaimed at a national meeting, "Ninety-five percent of all the granites I have ever walked over are magmatic!" (At least he didn't say 100 percent.) Today the argument has died down.

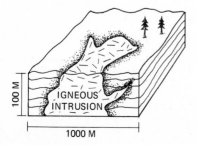

Figure 2-30 Contact metamorphism (dotted zone) occurs next to an igneous intrusion, largely because of the increased temperature and solutions from the intrusion. This diagrammatic intrusion has been exposed by erosion.

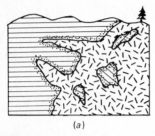   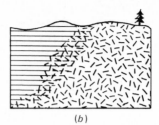

(a)   (b)

Figure 2-31   A magmatic granite is illustrated in (a); note the sharp contact, the contact metamorphism (shown by dots), the dikes of granite in the sedimentary rock, and the rotated blocks of sedimentary rock within the granite. (b) illustrates a granite which is the product of granitization; note the gradational contact, the lack of dikes, and the lack of rotated blocks.

Some granites with sharp contacts, contact metamorphism, and rotated inclusions or chunks of country rock in them are probably magmatic (Figure 2-31a). Others without sharp contacts, without contact metamorphism, and with inclusions that have the same orientations of internal features as the country rock probably are the result of granitization (Figure 2-31b). Some granite bodies apparently had two origins, with granitized zones around magmatic centers. (Now everybody should be happy!)

MINERAL RESOURCES

Mineral resources of the earth's crust are obviously of great importance to the human race. World economics, world politics, world history, and just plain, ordinary everyday living have been and are being influenced by these resources. The United States has been blessed with a general abundance and variety of mineral resources, and largely because of this, it is a leading industrial nation. We have all three major classes of mineral resources: fuels, metals, and nonmetals. All are essential, and while nonmetals such as limestone and sand are generally widely distributed, fuels and metals are not that common. Our use of these resources, which are essentially nonrenewable, is discussed in Chapter 9. Here, let's briefly consider the origins of these three classes of resources. You will note in the discussion that igneous, sedimentary, and metamorphic processes are involved in their formation.

Fuels—Fossil   Fossil fuels include coal, petroleum, and natural gas. All are organic in origin and consist of plant or animal remains which were deposited in sediments and are preserved in the sedimentary rock column after undergoing changes. The basis of this energy source is the process of photosynthesis, during which some of the sun's energy is captured and stored by green plants. This energy is present in both the plant kingdom and in the animal kingdom, which directly or indirectly relies on the plants for food.

The formation of peat, lignite, and coal is a straightforward process. As thick plant growth in swamps died and accumulated in the poorly oxygenated, stagnant swamp waters in which bacterial destruction of the plants was incomplete, layers of this organic material—leaves, twigs, and even tree trunks—accumulated as peat deposits. Burial by younger sediments provided the pressure to drive off water, hydrogen, oxygen, and other volatiles, transforming the peat into materials with a higher carbon content—lignite and higher-rank bituminous coal. Additional heat and pressure, usually provided by internal earth processes, can cause bituminous coal to be transformed into higher-rank anthracite coal, which contains very few volatiles.

Coal deposits, especially the lower-rank types, are very widespread as both relatively thick and thin beds. World reserves are estimated at several trillion tons. In Europe, coal seams as thin as 30 centimeters are being mined. In Wyoming, seams as thick as 30 meters are mined (Figure 2-32).

The origin of petroleum and natural gas is more complicated than the origin of coal. Basically, an oil or gas field results when four requirements are met: a source rock, a reservoir rock, a cap rock, and a natural trap. Most geologists think that the source "rock" of oil and gas is black mud in which each of billions of dead organisms left a microscopic droplet of oil. If the resulting oil and gas somehow move into a porous and permeable reservoir bed, such as a sandstone or porous limestone, then the potential for a valuable deposit exists. However, they will not be present in sufficient quantity until they are concentrated in some natural trap beneath an impermeable cap rock. Traps include upfolds (anticlines) in sedimentary

Figure 2-32 Coal mine at Kemmerer, Wyoming. Three seams of coal are visible, including a 30-meter-thick seam partially exposed in the bottom half of the photo. A total thickness of 90 meters of coal is present at this locality. The mine eventually will be 300 meters deep, 1.6 kilometers long, and 1 kilometer wide.

rocks, pinchouts of sand layers in muddy rocks, porous limestone reefs, salt domes, and fault traps. As both oil and gas are lighter than water, they accumulate in the upper parts of such traps (Figure 2-33). Note that some traps are the result of original depositional characteristics of the rock units, whereas the folds are the result of later deformation of the rocks.

Petroleum was first discovered by locating oil seeps on top of the ground and then searching for anticlines until the obvious anticlines were discovered. Finally, today, the search necessitates sophisticated geophysical techniques, especially wave reflection, which can locate and delineate buried traps. With the present scarcity of oil and gas, as will be discussed in Chapter 9, more effort is being devoted to getting as much petroleum out of a field as possible. Until recently, much was still left in a "pumped-out" field.

Two special types of petroleum deposits deserve a brief mention here, for they will be important in the near future. Oil shale is a dark, organic-rich shale found in quantity in the tristate area of Utah, Wyoming, and Colorado, where it was deposited in a large, ancient lake. The hydrocarbons are in a solid form rather than as oil. These hydrocarbons can be vaporized to produce as much as 100 gallons of oil per ton of shale; most, however, average about 30 gallons per ton. The tar sands of Alberta, Canada, contain a very heavy crude oil that is too viscous to flow naturally and must be removed by special processes. The recoverable oil from these two special types of deposits is apparently at least comparable to present United States and Canadian reserves of liquid petroleum.

Fuels—Nuclear   Uranium and thorium constitute the nuclear fuels, but to date we can utilize only the ^{235}U isotope of uranium, and this makes up less than 1 percent of natural uranium. Uranium ore is commonly found in sedimentary rocks, especially sandstones, where it has been deposited by groundwater seeping through the rocks. The waters originally dissolved the uranium out of igneous rocks and from veins of higher-grade uranium minerals. Canada's biggest reserves are in conglomerates and quartzites north of Lake Huron. Several areas of sedimentary rocks in the Western United States constitute our largest reserves. However, several rock units contain small amounts of uranium and thorium. The mining of large quantities of these rocks may be feasible (and necessary?) in the future.

Figure 2-33   Various types of oil traps with oil shown in black. (a) Anticline; (b) stratigraphic pinchout of sandstone beds in shale; (c) porous limestone reef; (d) traps adjacent to and above salt dome which penetrated and arched beds as it intruded; and (e) fault with oil trapped against impervious shale on opposite side of fault plane, or plane of movement.

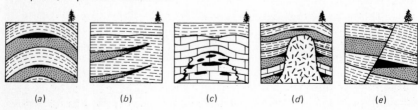

(a)   (b)   (c)   (d)   (e)

Metals   You will recall that about 99 percent of the earth's crust consists of only 8 elements (Table 2-2). The remaining 84 elements are quite rare and must be highly concentrated at places in the crust in order to be of value to human beings. For example, copper makes up about 0.000055 percent by weight of the earth's crust. We can mine deposits as low as 0.50 percent, but even this low-grade deposit requires a natural enrichment of 9000 times! It is indeed fortunate that nature has done this concentrating, for people would not have the available resources or energy to do it from scratch.

Nature has concentrated metals in several ways. Let us consider a few examples. Some deposits are the result of igneous activity. Some early formed metal-bearing minerals (e.g., copper or chromium minerals) may settle out of a magma and collect at the bottom of the cooling body. The world's largest nickel mine, at Sudbury, Ontario, Canada, may have had such an origin, but it has been suggested that Sudbury is an astrobleme, or star wound, and that the ore was at least mobilized by the heat of impact of a large meteorite.

Ions which do not fit into the common crystal structures because of their odd sizes or charges may be left over as magma cools and eventually may crystallize from watery solutions as veins or fracture fillings. The gold which prospectors search for in white hydrothermal (hot-water) quartz veins formed in this way, as did many other metals.

A number of rare metallic elements, such as tin, beryllium, zirconium, lithium, uranium, niobium, and yttrium, are found in the minerals of coarse-grained igneous rocks called pegmatites, which crystallized from the last watery portions of magmas. Some crystals in pegmatites are as much as 12 meters long! The ions can easily move through the very fluid magma to sites of crystal growth.

Many of the world's high-grade deposits of copper, zinc, lead, silver, and gold are closely associated with ancient volcanic rocks or with present-day volcanic island arcs. The exact origins of these ores are a subject of debate, but no one argues against the volcanic association. The major copper deposits of the world are low-grade (as low as 0.5 percent is mined) copper deposits disseminated through certain types of intermediate to felsic pluton-ic rocks (Figure 2-34).

Weathering results in several metal deposits. Bauxite ($Al_2O_3 \cdot H_2O$), the ore of aluminum, is the result of a very thorough weathering of clay minerals under the right chemical conditions in a subtropical or tropical climate.

The major iron-ore deposits of the world are the result of the freeing of iron from source rocks by weathering and its deposition in layers in ancient seas (Figure 2-35). The exact origin of these layers is a problem: Did primitive microscopic organisms cause the iron compounds to precipitate from seawater or were iron oxide particles washed into the sea? Most of the major iron formations were deposited as low-grade units containing 25 to 30 percent iron and much chert (SiO_2). Later, slightly acid groundwaters moved through cracks in the iron formation and dissolved the chert, leaving higher-grade iron deposits, chiefly hematite (Fe_2O_3). These high-grade ores in the Lake Superior region were instrumental in making the United States an industrial giant, with more than 4 billion tons shipped to date. The steel

Figure 2-34 Bingham Canyon Mine near Salt Lake City, Utah. The pit is more than 600 meters deep. About 385,000 metric tons of rock are mined each day; of this, about 100,000 metric tons are ore which runs 0.64 percent copper. Molybdenum, gold, silver, and other elements are produced as by-products. The Wasatch Mountains are in the background. *(Photo courtesy of Utah Copper Division, Kennecott Copper Corporation.)*

industry now utilizes the original low-grade iron formation, called taconite. The taconite is crushed to a very fine size, the magnetic iron-ore particles (magnetite) are separated by magnets, and the particles are bound into high-grade pellets. Taconite pellets, which are preferred by the steel industry over "chunk ore" because they speed up the steel-making process, are rapidly replacing the high-grade ores, which are nearly mined out.

The processes of sedimentation may mechanically concentrate such minerals as gold; running water sorts sediment not only by size but also by weight. Particles of native gold, which is many times heavier than the common rock-forming minerals, may be concentrated together to form placer deposits. Several other minerals, including diamonds and other heavy gemstones, are also found in placers.

The gold rush of 1849 in California was started when Jim Marshall found placer gold at Sutter's mill on the American River in 1848. One nugget weighed 88.6 kilograms (195 pounds); that would have been worth about $600,000 at late-1974 prices ($195 per ounce). The rush died out 20 years later after $850 million of gold had been panned from the streams (Figure 2-36). To date, $1.3 billion worth of gold has been mined from California placer deposits.

Figure 2-35   Iron-ore mine in Minnesota. This photo was taken a few decades ago when most mines were in high-grade ore. Low-grade taconite ore is now being mined as the high-grade ores are being depleted. *(Courtesy of United States Steel Corporation.)*

Figure   2-36 Panning   for gold in Alaska, 1900. *(Courtesy of A. H. Brooks, United States Geological Survey.)*

Later, miners used great jets of water to wash down thick layers of ancient stream deposits in the same area. The loosened sediment washed downstream and ruined agricultural lands and navigation in rivers. Finally, the Anti-debris Act of 1884 outlawed the water jets; this was one of the earlier cases of a law being passed to preserve the environment. Eventually, the gold-bearing gravels were traced upstream to the Mother Lode, a large system of hydrothermal gold-bearing quartz veins on the west side of the Sierra Nevada, and numerous mines produced gold here.

Nonmetals While much less glamorous than metals or fossil fuels, nonmetallic mineral resources are essential to our society and nearly equal the metallics in value. Most of the major nonmetallic deposits have a sedimentary origin. Limestone, marble, and shale are used in the manufacture of cement. Sands and gravels from old river or beach deposits are used as aggregate in concrete construction. Clay from marine and nonmarine beds is used in the making of brick, tile, pipe, pottery, and dishware. Phosphate deposits ($CaPO_4$) originally precipitated in marine waters are widely used as fertilizer. Both salt (which is necessary for life) and gypsum ($CaSO_4 \cdot 2H_2O$), a major ingredient in plaster and cement, are formed by the evaporation of isolated bodies of seawater. Building stones include plutonic rocks (e.g., granite), sedimentary rocks (e.g., limestone, dolostone, and sandstone), and metamorphic rocks (e.g., gneiss and marble). A few nonmetallic minerals have a metamorphic origin; talc, used in talcum powder, and asbestos, used in fireproof materials, are both formed by the metamorphism of magnesium-bearing rocks.

Go my sons—burn your books—buy yourselves stout shoes—go to the mountains—search the valleys—the deserts—the shores of the seas—the deepest recesses of the earth. In this way, and no other, will you arrive at a knowledge of things and of their properties.

Petrus Severinus (1571)

THREE

EARTH'S INTERNAL PROCESSES AND EFFECTS

Most of us, because of where we live, probably think of the earth as a rather silent, stable sphere in space. Sure, it's rotating on its axis and it's revolving around the sun, but otherwise it seems, as a whole, quite dead. Nothing could be further from the truth—the earth is literally full of energy. Volcanoes erupt every year somewhere on its surface, both on land and beneath the sea. We hear about only one or two really bad earthquakes each year, yet there are probably more than a million per year which are strong enough to be felt if people were situated in the right places to feel them. Mountains are being built even today as they were in the past, but the rate of uplift is so slow relative to a person's lifetime that the process isn't even noticed. In some areas in California, the Coast Ranges are rising a meter per century.

Some other places in the world are undergoing a broad, gentle upwarping or downwarping. Western Finland is now rising out of the sea at a rate of nearly 1 centimeter a year; the rate has slowed, for uplift has totaled 275 meters in the last 12,000 years. In Italy, the seaside ruins of a Roman building constructed more than 2000 years ago contain holes of a boring clam; the land on which the building is located must have subsided below sea level and then again risen above sea level, all in the past 2000 years. Yet, probably no Roman or Italian perceived this movement of the land. An ancient beach along the Minnesota shore of Lake Superior is 220 meters above the present lake level at Duluth, which is located at the western tip of the lake, and is 275 meters above lake level 250 kilometers farther to the northeast; clearly the area has been tilted during the 11,500 years since the beach was abandoned by a shrinking lake.

A final and much grander example of earth movement has come to light in the past few decades. The earth's crust apparently consists of half a dozen or so major pieces, or plates, which are moving either toward each other, past each other, or away from each other at the rate of a few centimeters per year. This is an exceedingly short distance relative to the circumference of the earth and may seem inconsequential. But even at this slow rate over a long period of time—200 million years—the entire Atlantic Ocean was created.

So we don't live on a tired and rundown old Mother Earth: she is instead vibrant, fiery, and exciting. And her actions directly affect mankind; in the last thousand years an estimated 3 to 5 million people have lost their lives in earthquakes and volcanic eruptions. Let's study Ms. Earth's actions in more detail.

VOLCANISM

The volcanic island of Krakatoa, between Java and Sumatra in the East Indies, had been quiet for more than 200 years when, on August 27, 1883, four great volcanic explosions occurred. One of the explosions was probably the greatest the earth has ever experienced: it was heard more than 5000 kilometers away! Steam and volcanic ash were blown to an estimated height of 80 kilometers and came down over an area of 775,000 square kilometers. Much of the dust which reached the high-level jetstream circled the earth for 2 years, causing spectacular sunsets all over the world. It even caused climatic changes. Europe's crops were especially poor for the next 2 years. Before the explosions, Krakatoa had had an 800-meter-high volcano on it; after the explosions, only a deep sea existed. About 75 cubic kilometers of volcanic material "disappeared." Where could it have gone? Some clearly went up with the explosion, but geologists figure that much of it must have collapsed into the underlying magma chamber, forming a large crater called a caldera. Curiously, it was not the explosion itself that did the most damage, but a great 30-meter-high sea wave which hit the shores of Java and Sumatra, up to 80 kilometers away, killing an estimated 40,000 people. And Krakatoa is rebuilding: a volcano called Anak Krakatoa, or "child of Krakatoa," has been growing sporadically since 1927.

The East Indies are densely populated; Java has more people per square kilometer than any other area in the world. Other volcanic areas are also heavily populated. Why do people live in such dangerous areas? One reason is that the soils which quickly form on the porous volcanic ash are very rich in nutrients. So volcanoes have both good and bad points.

There are three main types of volcanoes. The large symmetrical cones which we commonly think of when we hear the word volcano are *composite cones*, made up of alternating layers of pyroclastic ("fire-broken") particles thrown out by explosions and flows of rather viscous intermediate-to-felsic lava (Figure 3-1). The many high peaks of the Cascade Range in our Pacific Northwest are composite cones (Figure 3-2).

Figure 3-1 Mount Rainier, Washington. *(Courtesy of J. Kotar.)*

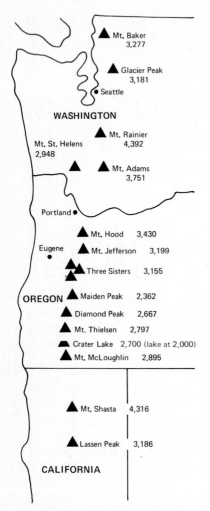

Figure 3-2   The Cascade Range. Elevations are given in meters. While only Mount Lassen has erupted recently (minor activity in 1914 to 1917), Mount Shasta, Mount St. Helens, and Mount Baker have acted up in the last 2000 years. Mount Hood and Crater Lake figure in Indian legends; Crater Lake formed when Mount Mazama erupted and collapsed into its magma chamber about 6600 years ago. Mount Rainier lets off steam. *(After Howel Williams, 1941. Crater Lake: The Story of its Origin, University of California Press.)*

Shield volcanoes are broad, low volcanoes. The magma of shield volcanoes is basaltic and has a low viscosity. Because of its fluidity such lava flows outward from the vents, sometimes at tens of kilometers per hour. Our best examples are in the Hawaiian Islands, a 2500-kilometer-long chain of volcanoes. The island of Hawaii is built of five volcanoes, including Mauna Loa, which is 150 kilometers across and more than 4200 meters above sea level (Figure 3-3). [As the sea here has a depth of about 5000 meters, Mauna Loa is actually higher than Mount Everest (8848 meters above sea level), the highest mountain on land.] Divers in Hawaii have found that lava which reaches the sea commonly forms pillows as it rapidly cools. In fact, pillows in ancient volcanic rocks provide geologists with evidence of subaqueous deposition (Figure 3-4).

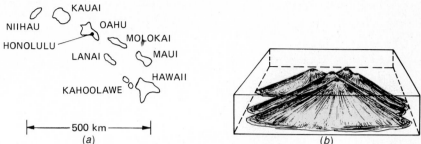

KAUAI
NIIHAU
OAHU
HONOLULU
MOLOKAI
LANAI
MAUI
HAWAII
KAHOOLAWE

|←——————— 500 km ———————→|
(a)   (b)

Figure 3-3 (a) Part of the 2500-kilometer-long Hawaiian Islands chain. (b) The island of Hawaii. The vertical scale is exaggerated on the diagram.

A third and smaller type of volcano is a *cinder cone*, made up entirely of pyroclastic particles, many of them glassy or cindery in appearance. Cinder cones are abundant in many spots in the Western United States (Figure 3-5) and in Mexico. Paricutin erupted in a Mexican cornfield in 1943 and grew to a height of about 600 meters during its 9 years of activity. It provided a natural laboratory for geologists who monitored its every action.

Where are the world's 500 or so presently active volcanoes? Most make up the Ring of Fire, which circles the Pacific Ocean; the second concentration is along an east-west belt which extends from the Mediterranean Sea eastward into Asia. Most of the remaining volcanoes are found in the ocean basins, along the subsea ridges. Probably the most famous volcano is Surtsey, which rose from the sea south of Iceland in 1963. This pattern of volcano distribution, while long a puzzle to geologists, can now be explained

Figure 3-4 Pillowed basalts like these in Canada, provide evidence of formation underwater.

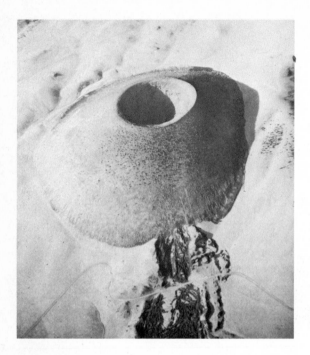

Figure 3-5 S. P. Crater in Arizona, an excellent example of a cinder cone. The cone is 273 meters high. It is estimated to be about 70,000 years old. (Its name is an abbreviation of a colorful term.) A lava flow has extruded near the base of the cone. *(Courtesy of R. G. Updike.)*

by modern plate tectonic theory. We will return to this subject later in this chapter.

Can we tell when a volcano is going to erupt? Usually there is some warning that the earth has indigestion: a few belches, some passed gas. Also, the earth quite commonly vibrates before eruptions. During the 24 hours before Kilauea volcano on Hawaii erupted in 1959, 2200 small earthquakes were recorded on the flanks of the volcano. Monte Somma, the predecessor to modern Mount Vesuvius (near Naples, Italy), gave out signals of internal unrest even after being inactive for 800 years. When it showed signs of activity (earthquakes) in A.D. 63, few people became worried. They should have, however, because 16 years later, the Roman resort city of Pompeii, on the blue Mediterranean at the foot of Monte Somma, was buried by 8 to 10 meters of volcanic ash; 2000 people died (Figure 3-6). (But who wants to leave one's home behind because of what may be a false alarm?) In that eruption, Pliny the Elder, a leading Roman naturalist, philosopher, historian, and admiral of a fleet anchored in the nearby Bay of Naples, went ashore for a closer look at the spectacle, and became one of the victims. (His nephew, Pliny the Younger, reportedly stayed on ship to complete his schoolwork, and hence survived.) Pompeii's sister resort city (Herculaneum) was buried beneath muddy volcanic ash flows which were hot enough to char logs.

One of the best approaches to predicting volcanic eruptions is a thorough study of active volcanoes. Knowing this, scientists have operated volcanic observatories at many locations around the world, including Mount Vesuvius since 1845 and Hawaii since 1912. Tiltmeters, essentially long

Figure 3-6 Pompeii with Mount Vesuvius (left) and the remains of Monte Somma (right) in the background. Excavation of the city has revealed many details about the life in a Roman city, including some that cannot be mentioned here.

U-shaped tubes of water that can measure a tilt of 2.5 centimeters in 110 kilometers, have been in use in Japan and Hawaii; the slight bulging caused by magma moving closer to the surface can sometimes be detected in this way or by careful surveying. The temperatures in drill holes may change, as can the magnetism of an area.

Mudflows moving down from volcanoes are commonly more dangerous than the actual eruptions. Volcanic activity on snow-covered volcanoes, or monsoon rains eroding loose volcanic debris, can cause such mudflows. One in Ecuador moved 240 kilometers at an average speed of 27 kilometers per hour, and some have been clocked at nearly 100 kilometers per hour. One from Mount Rainier in Washington covered part of the now heavily populated Puget Sound lowland 5000 years ago; it could happen again.

Not all magma that reaches the surface comes out of vents at the tops of volcanoes. Tremendous volumes have poured out along great systems of cracks in the earth's crust. The Columbia Plateau in the Northwestern United States (Figure 3-7) is the result of such volcanism. Whereas individual flows are as thin as 3 meters, the total pile is generally 1500 meters thick and locally as much as 4 kilometers thick. The flows together cover more than 500,000 square kilometers. Most of these poured out between 10 and 25 million years ago. However, the Craters of the Moon National Monument in Idaho may contain the last volcanic activity on the plateau; soil hasn't even developed on these rocks yet, and so they are probably only 1000 to 2000 years old. A much older example in the Lake Superior region is described in Chapter 7.

In 1783, eruptions from similar cracks occurred in Iceland. Basalt poured out of 32-kilometer-long Laki Fissure and covered more than 560 square

(a)

(b)

Figure 3-7 (a) The Columbia Plateau. (b) A number of lava flows in the Columbia Plateau. *(Courtesy of P. Hooper.)*

kilometers. Ten thousand people and most of Iceland's livestock perished. However, at the time, most deaths were attributed to the volcanic gases and the ensuing poor crops. And that was not the end. Iceland has had 14 volcanic eruptions in this century; the last time was in January 1973.

Some areas of relatively recent volcanic activity contain hot springs and geysers. The word *geyser* comes from the Icelandic word *geysir*, meaning "gusher." Yellowstone Park is part of the Yellowstone Rhyolite Plateau, which was volcanically active as recently as 60,000 years ago. In the park, surface water moves down cracks, encounters hot rock at depth, and returns to the surface as superheated steam and spectacular eruptions from the 200 geysers, as well as from 3000 hot springs. The "piping" would probably give a plumber nightmares (Figure 3-8).

EARTHQUAKES

On Good Friday, 1964, one of the greatest earthquakes of all time shook half of Alaska and caused the entire earth to vibrate slightly. Swimming pools sloshed in Texas, and water rose and fell in water wells as far away as Puerto Rico and Denmark. If people had been distributed in all directions from the earthquake center, it would have been felt over an area of about 2.6 million square kilometers (1 million square miles)! The energy released was equal to about $31\frac{1}{2}$ million tons of TNT. Naturally, United States Geological Survey geologists hurried in to study the effects of the earthquake. Near the earthquake center in southern Alaska, tops of trees were snapped off, mountain glaciers surged forward, rockslides moved down mountains, ice cracked or buckled on lakes over an area of nearly 260,000 square kilometers, and land rose or fell a meter or more over an area of 88,000 square kilometers. Kodiak Island sank nearly 2 meters. Over the next 3 days, 52 main aftershocks, or additional earthquakes, occurred in the same area, but all were of lesser magnitude.

Fortunately Alaska is sparsely populated and only 114 people were killed; however, property damage amounted to $750 million, mainly because of numerous landslides triggered by the earthquakes (Figure 3-9). If such a large earthquake had occurred in a densely populated area, the results would have been disastrous. The Lisbon, Portugal, earthquake of 1755 killed 30,000 people and was so severe that chandeliers rattled in the 13 colonies. In the 1923 Tokyo-Yokohama earthquake in Japan, nearly 150,000 people were killed and half a million buildings were destroyed. Since, on the average, about 18 to 20 major earthquakes occur in the world each year, it is quite likely that a truly devastating one will occur during your lifetime.

As a result of the Alaskan earthquake, a tsunami, or seismic sea wave, traveled from Alaska to Japan, Hawaii, and California; 14 persons were killed in Crescent City, California, 2700 kilometers away, where the wave was 4 meters high. This was a small tsunami; one 64 meters high was once recorded as the result of an earthquake near Japan.

Earthquakes, like volcanoes, take place most frequently along certain zones, or *belts*. Most occur around the Pacific Ocean; it has been estimated that 80 percent of earthquake energy is released along this zone (Figure

Figure 3-8 Old Faithful geyser in Yellowstone National Park. It erupts about once every hour for about 5 minutes and throws out about 40,000 liters of water each time. It has never failed to erupt on schedule; we just do not always know its schedule.

3-10). Other major zones are along the Mid-Atlantic Ridge and the Mid-Indian Ocean Ridge. (Do these belts sound familiar? More later. . . .) The worst earthquake in the Western Hemisphere, in terms of direct fatalities, was that on February 4, 1976, in Guatemala, where about 19,000 persons died.

Is the United States safe? Well, in 1972, 22 of our 50 United States experienced a total of 282 "feelable" quakes; California led with 117, Alaska had 113, Montana 19, Utah 7, and Hawaii 4. Thus it seems that most of the

Figure 3-9 Landslides in Anchorage caused by Alaska earthquake of March 1964. Five years earlier, U.S. Geological Survey geologists had warned against building on the clay slopes. *(Courtesy of U.S. Army.)*

area of the United States is indeed quite safe in this regard, but probably no state is completely immune. For example, the New Madrid, Missouri, earth-quake of 1811 was comparable to the Alaskan quake just described. It rang church bells and stopped clocks in Boston, was felt from Canada to the Gulf of Mexico and from the Rockies to the Atlantic, and caused major topograph-

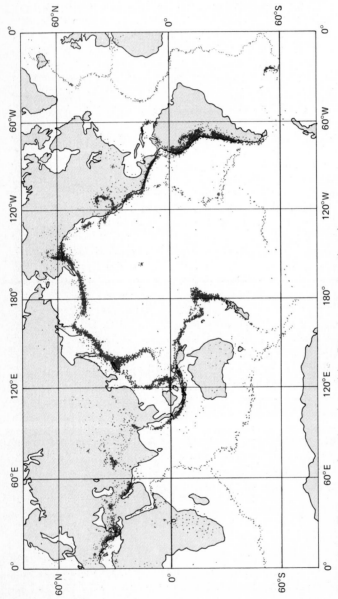

Figure 3-10 The zones of earthquake activity. Dots represent earthquakes.

ic changes over 130,000 square kilometers. More than 1800 aftershocks were felt over the next 3 months! However, only six persons were killed, and Daniel Boone, already an old man, was *not* one of them.

What causes the earth to quake, or vibrate, anyway? As we have already implied in connection with volcanoes, some quakes are due to movements in and around magma chambers. Most, however, are due to movement along faults in the outer layers of the earth. During the San Francisco earthquake of 1906, for example, there was locally as much as 6 meters of horizontal movement along the San Andreas fault zone; roads and fences were offset by this or a lesser amount (Figure 3-11). More commonly, movement along a fault occurs at depth and little evidence of that movement can be observed at the surface.

The best explanation of what happens during an earthquake is provided by the *elastic-rebound theory*. Strain accumulates along a fault owing to earth pressures, but because of the friction of the rocks on one side of the fault against those on the other side of the fault, movement is not possible until the pressure becomes great enough to overcome the friction. Meanwhile, the rocks on both sides of the fault bend as they are accumulating the strain, and once movement occurs they *snap* back elastically to an unstrained position with a *bang*, which causes the earth tremors. The rocks on the two sides of the fault, however, then have slightly different relative locations, the difference being the amount of movement along the fault.

Detailed measurements are continuously being taken along and across the San Andreas fault zone. Geophysicists have wisely set up detection equipment at Hollister, California (Figure 3-11*a*), in a winery which is slowly being torn in two because it was built in 1948 straddling a fault. Another winery located on the same spot was destroyed in the 1906 San Francisco earthquake. The winery owners obviously knew little about the geology of the area or they would never have relocated the winery on the fault. However, it is a place where the movement of the San Andreas over the past few decades can be readily observed. The winery is now acclaimed as absolutely the best last stop of geological field trips in California.

These and related studies show relative movement of a few centimeters per year of rocks on opposite sides of the zone. In places the few centimeters are taken up by movement during earthquakes along one of many faults in the zone, and in other places the strain is evidently building up until the friction can be overcome. So we can certainly anticipate more earthquakes. Small earthquakes along a fault system may mean that the small earthquakes are acting as safety valves, releasing the pressure before it can accumulate enough to cause a large earthquake. Or, small earthquakes may be heralding initial slippage before a big movement and a big earthquake.

Can scientists predict when earthquakes will occur? Earthquake prediction is certainly a worthwhile objective, for many large population centers exist along seismically active zones, as in California and Japan. In fact, about a third of the population of the United States lives in areas of high earthquake potential. But what would happen if it was announced that an earthquake might occur in a given area in the next few days or weeks? Much education of

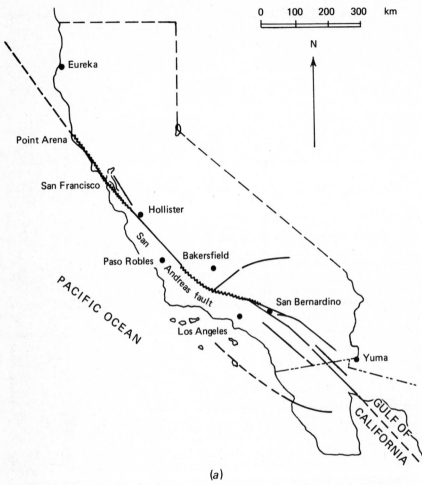

0   100   200   300   km

N

Eureka

Point Arena

San Francisco

Hollister

Paso Robles   Bakersfield

San

Andreas fault

PACIFIC OCEAN

Los Angeles

San Bernardino

Yuma

GULF OF CALIFORNIA

(a)

Figure 3-11 (a) The San Andreas fault zone and some related faults in California. (b) The San Andreas fault in the Carrizo Plain, San Luis Obispo County. View is to the south. *(Courtesy of R. E. Wallace, United States Geological Survey.)*

the public is undoubtedly necessary! And it seems that the world's scientists will soon be able to make such predictions. For example, they have found that before seismic activity begins, changes occur in local sea level, water levels and radon gas content change in wells, the strength of the earth's magnetic field changes, and the detailed behavioral characteristics of rocks in the area change.

Earthquakes are detected by *seismographs* which essentially are instruments with one part anchored to bedrock, thereby shaking when the bedrock shakes, and another part "suspended" in space, thereby remaining motionless when an earthquake occurs (Figure 3-12). The record of this shaking

(b)

is a *seismogram* (Figure 3-12). The seismogram is marked P, S, and L, designating the main different types of seismic waves.

The L wave is a long wave or surface wave; these cause the major damage during an earthquake. The P and S waves are body waves which travel through the earth rather than near its surface; these are waves scientists are most interested in, for they provide important information on earthquakes and on the nature of the earth's interior. The motions of the two types of body waves are shown in Figure 3-13. The P wave is the fastest wave and appears first on a seismogram. On the basis of many measurements of earthquakes and laboratory experiments, geophysicists know how fast the P and S waves travel, permitting them to draw travel-time curves. Thus, if the S

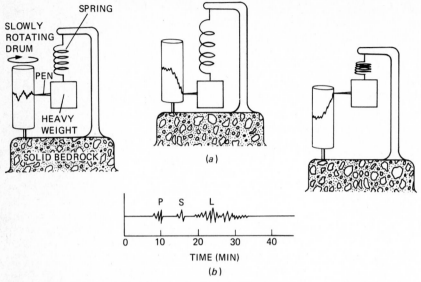

Figure 3-12 Seismograph (a) and seismogram (b).

Figure 3-13 (a) Movement of particles of matter as a P wave, or "push-pull" wave, moves through rock. In the upper diagram, the rock is at rest; the lower two diagrams illustrate the movement of particles as the wave passes through the rock. Movement of an individual particle is shown by the black dots. (b) Movement of particles of matter as an S wave, or "shake" wave, moves through rock. In the upper diagram, the rock is at rest; the lower two diagrams illustrate the movement of particles as the wave passes through the rock. Movement of an individual particle is shown by the black dots.

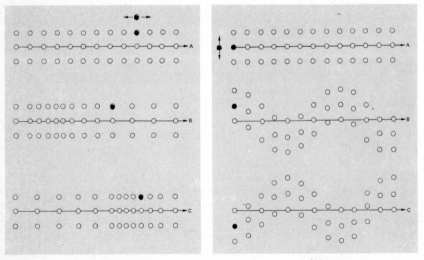

wave arrives at a seismograph 5 minutes later than the P wave, as in Figure 3-12, it is a simple matter to go to the travel-time curves to see how far it is to the *epicenter*, or point on the earth's surface directly above the *focus*, or actual spot at which the earthquake occurs. In the illustration used, the epicenter is about 4000 kilometers away. The foci of most earthquakes are located at depths of 8 to 30 kilometers, but some are as deep as 700 kilometers, suggesting that the rocks are still rigid at that depth. We will return to the depth data later.

A single seismograph station will show only the distance to an epicenter; it does not distinguish direction. Therefore, three stations are necessary to locate an earthquake (Figure 3-14).

The amount of energy released in an earthquake is measured from several seismograms, and is commonly expressed in terms of the Richter scale, named after a Cal Tech seismologist-geologist who developed it. The scale extends from 0 to 10 and is logarithmic; for each unit of 1 on the scale, the energy released increases by more than 30 times over the next lower whole number. Thus, an earthquake of Richter magnitude 5 releases about 30 times as much energy as one with a magnitude of 4 (Table 3-1).

The greatest earthquake ever measured had a magnitude of 8.6; the 1906 San Francisco earthquake is estimated at 8.3; the 1964 Alaskan earthquake described above had a magnitude of 8.5 (twice the energy of the San Francisco earthquake); the Guatemala earthquake of February 1976 had a magnitude of 7.5. A reading of 7 or more on the scale usually indicates a major destructive earthquake. Magnitudes of 2 are strong enough to be felt.

Figure 3-14 An earthquake can be located if it is recorded at three different seismograph stations. (Would two stations suffice?) This earthquake occurred in Central America.

Table 3-1 Richter scale of earthquake magnitude*

EARTHQUAKE MAGNITUDE	APPROXIMATE ENERGY RELEASED (TNT)
1.0	6 ounces
2.0	13 pounds
3.0	397 pounds
4.0	6 tons
5.0	199 tons
6.0	6,270 tons
7.0	199,000 tons
8.0	6,270,000 tons
9.0	199,000,000 tons

*From *Geology* by William C. Putnam, revised by Ann Bradley Bassett. Copyright © 1964, 1971 by Oxford University Press, Inc. Reprinted by permission.

EARTH'S INTERIOR

The time it takes seismic waves to travel through the earth and arrive at a seismograph station from earthquakes at varying distances from the station helps to show that rock density within the earth increases with depth. P and S waves are reflected or refracted (changed in direction) as they meet zones of different kinds of material within the earth, and also undergo increases in velocity at certain depths. They travel along arc-shaped routes (Figure 3-15). These data define distinct boundaries within the earth which delineate zones of material of differing wave velocity. The three major zones are the *crust*, the *mantle*, and the *core*. The *Moho*, or Mohorovicíc boundary between the crust and the mantle, is the best known of the boundaries.

The Core   If an earthquake occurs more than 11,000 kilometers (about 7000 miles) away from a seismograph station, the S waves never arrive. Why not? And in a 5000-kilometer-wide zone, or ring, around the earth between 11,000 and 16,000 kilometers from an epicenter, neither the P or S waves arrive, creating what is called a blind, or shadow, zone (Figure 3-15). Why? And at distances greater than 16,000 kilometers from an epicenter, the P waves again arrive, although they arrive "late." Why?

Geophysicists, utilizing all these data and their model of the earth, have an explanation for these incidents. The nature of P waves is such that they can travel through any material, whereas S waves by their nature can move only through rigid (solid) material. The boundary between the mantle and the core is at such a depth that S waves traveling their arc-shaped paths can travel 11,000 kilometers without hitting the core. Beyond that distance their routes would take them through the core. Since they don't make it beyond 11,000 kilometers, the logical conclusion, although indirect, is that the core is liquid, completely damping out the S waves and slowing the P waves. And the amount of tardiness of the P waves shows that the entire thickness of the core cannot be liquid, for if the P waves had to travel slowly through all that liquid, they would arrive still later than they do. Thus, geophysicists think that the inner core is solid, with a liquid outer core.

Recall from Chapter 1 that earth has a density of 5.52 and that surface

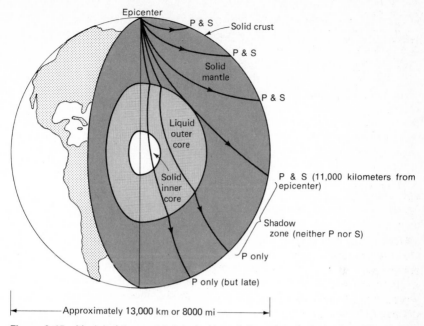

Figure 3-15   Model of the earth's interior, largely based on the behavior of earthquake waves at depth. Also shown is a hypothetical earthquake and the movement of waves away from the epicenter.

rocks have a density of about 2.7 to 3.0. The interior must therefore be composed of heavier material. Calculations which assume that the earth's core, both the liquid outer and solid inner portions, is made of iron with some nickel (plus a little sulfur and silicon) satisfy the density requirements. The fact that most metallic meteorites are iron-nickel types and presumably come from the asteroid belt of our own solar system provides additional indirect support for this model.

The Mantle   The zone beneath the Moho is called the mantle and is also divided into subzones of differing velocities. While it is true that there is a general increase in seismic wave velocity with depth, there is one important exception. In the upper part of the mantle is a low-velocity layer called the *asthenosphere* (weak sphere), in which seismic waves travel more slowly than in rock above and below it. This is a low-strength "plastic" layer beneath the rigid lithosphere of upper mantle and crust, and presumably this layer can "flow," or move, slowly. It is thus a key layer in modern plate tectonic theory, providing a zone of weakness along which the overlying rigid plates of lithosphere can move. Geophysicists think it is a low-velocity layer because there is melting in scattered pockets, there is some water in the minerals, and the other minerals in the zone are near their melting points. The S waves are slowed down more than the P waves when passing through the asthenosphere, thereby supporting this idea.

The mantle as a whole is presumably composed of ultramafic rocks, made up largely of the minerals olivine, pyroxene, calcium-plagioclase, and garnet. Stony meteorites have similar compositions, and like the metallic ones, most presumably originated in our own solar system.

You may have heard of the Mohole Project. Scientists back in 1959 developed a scheme (reportedly at a cocktail party) for drilling nearly 10 kilometers through the water (the easy part), through the thin oceanic crust, and into the mantle, in order to bring up samples of mantle material. A floating drilling platform was developed and some test holes were drilled near Hawaii. However, the project became a political boondoggle, evidently the space program and Viet Nam took priority, even the original scientists (who had been relegated to advisory status) wanted the idea dropped, and the project was shelved after considerable expenditures. Postponement of the project must have been a relief to some anxious citizens who worried about the effects of drilling such a deep hole. One said, "If the inside of the earth is hot, the water running in it is going to generate a lot of steam that will blow up the planet." Another wrote, "Below the crust the earth is hollow, a great big vacuum chamber, so when you punch a hole into this vacuum, the earth is going to implode or explode inward." One, who was probably the most deeply worried citizen, stated, "Hell's down there, mister, so when you dig that hole you're gonna loose the fires, to say nothing of all those devils." (It was one project, according to a sage observer, in which the American taxpayer could literally see his money going down a hole in the ground. Yet the scientific benefits could have been great, and offshore drilling technology may have benefited, too.)

The Crust The rock at the earth's surface and extending down to the Moho is called the crust. Obviously, this is the layer which we know best, for we can make many direct observations on the relationships of one rock type to another. Chapter 2, on "Earth Materials," might have been better named "Crustal Materials."

By direct observation and sampling at the surface and by deeper sampling via drilling, we know that the crustal rocks of continents are basically different from those of the ocean floors. Whereas the dominant rock of continents is *granitic*, the dominant rock of ocean basins is *basaltic*. Both continents and ocean floors also have sediments or sedimentary rocks present, but we have already learned in Chapter 2 that, while sediments are widespread, they are volumetrically minor.

Seismic-wave studies provide us with additional information on the crust, confirming that the continents are granitic, that the ocean basins are basaltic, and that the crustal thickness varies from 5 kilometers beneath the oceans to as much as 60 to 70 kilometers beneath the continents (Figure 3-16). These studies also reveal that the basaltic layer of the oceans passes beneath the continents as well, although the discontinuity between the granitic and basaltic layers is not easily recognized everywhere.

The seismic waves also reveal that the crust beneath higher parts of the earth's surface—mountains and plateaus—is thicker than beneath lower-lying plains. Thus, mountains have "roots" (Figure 3-16), much as do

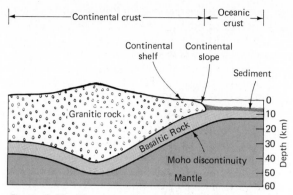

Figure 3-16 Diagrammatic model of continental and oceanic crust.

icebergs, which are about 90 percent beneath the water's surface. This idea, that the higher blocks of the earth's crust also project lower, and that different blocks ride, or "float," on heavier material at an equilibrium level, is called *isostasy*.

Isostasy was suggested by Archdeacon J. H. Pratt in India in the mid-1800s after a detailed land survey of India revealed a small error between two survey methods, one a system of intersecting lines and triangles and the other based on astronomical observations. Pratt suggested that the error might be due to the gravitational attraction of the Himalaya Mountains on the hanging plumb bob, essentially a weight on a string, of the instrument used to take sights on the stars. (Presumably a plumb bob should point straight toward the earth's center because of gravitational attraction of the earth, thereby giving the true vertical. The perpendicular to this hanging plumb bob should have given the true horizontal from which the angular sights to the stars were made.)

Calculations showed that the deflection of the Himalayas should be more than the actual deflection. Pratt reasoned that the lesser deflection was a result of light rock projecting to depth beneath the mountain—hence, roots. He added that rocks beneath mountains were lighter than those beneath plains, which were lighter than those beneath low-lying ocean basins. Sir G. B. Airy, about the same time, suggested that continental rocks were similar under both mountains and plains, and that the crust was simply thicker beneath mountains and thinner beneath plains. This has, of course, been verified by seismic studies. Modern workers have added a further modification based on seismic data: the rocks within each block of crust become somewhat heavier at depth. Isostasy is a very important theory in geology and was a great help in understanding mountains.

DEFORMATION OF THE CRUST

If you were to walk along a sandy beach and reflect on the nature of the sand layer, might you conclude, as Nicholas Steno did in Europe in 1669, that the layer of sand was deposited in a subhorizontal position? Further contemplation might lead you to realize that the position of this sand layer is due to the action of water and the effect of gravity on the sand.

Now if you were to leave the beach and walk high up a nearby mountain side, and there saw beds of sandstone in a vertical rather than a subhorizontal position, you would surely realize by applying the principle of "the present is the key to the past" that something is awry. Those vertical sandstone beds are not in their original positions. Why not? And how did beds of sand ever become located high up on a mountain?

If upon close inspection of the sandstone beds you found them to contain fossil oyster shells, what would be your conclusion? Probably the same one Leonardo da Vinci reached in the late 1400s when he found marine fossils high in the mountains of Lombardy. He said something like this: "These rocks were once beds of sand on the sea floor—they have since been hardened and uplifted to form these mountains."

Unfortunately, the great logic you've just displayed is a few hundred years too late to excite anyone. But in the days of da Vinci and Steno, and on into the middle of the nineteenth century, such statements were interpreted by many as being in direct opposition to the creation story in Genesis. Such speculations, of course, implied that rocks were of different ages and that more time than the 6 days of creation was involved in their formation.

James Hutton of Scotland became the center of much of the controversy in the 1790s because his observations had convinced him that a great amount of time must have been available to form the rocks and the relationships which he was studying. Consequently he made what is probably the most repeated quote in geology: "I see no vestige of a beginning—no sign of the end." This was, of course, heresy, for if there was no beginning, there was no Creator! But Hutton had correctly realized that the geological features he was observing—folded and twisted rocks, broken rocks with evidence of movement along the cracks, and horizontal rocks on top of tilted rocks—all indicated that the earth's history was considerably longer than 6000 years, as calculated from other Biblical interpretations (Figure 3-17).

Folds The original horizontality of beds of sedimentary rock as noted by Steno is commonly disturbed by compressive earth forces which cause the beds to become folded. As the pressures which cause the folding act slowly over a long period of time, most rocks can absorb the strain and bend without breaking. The result is upfolds, or *anticlines* (Figure 3-18), and downfolds, or *synclines*. Generally they occur together in an alternating arrangement.

If the folds are formed in an area which is being uplifted, and this is commonly so, then erosion occurs. This exposes the beds within the folds, and the result is a pattern of concentric rock layers which can be traced around the fold (Figure 3-19). Observation of the directions of dip of the tilted beds in such eroded folds will reveal whether they are eroded anticlines or synclines. (How?) Or, if the relative ages of the rock units involved in the folding are known, it is again a simple matter to determine the type of fold. (How? Your answer should involve the principle of superposition.) Students commonly think all anticlines are hills and all synclines are valleys, but this is

Figure 3-17 James Hutton in 1787 observed these horizontal rocks above vertical rocks in Scotland. He correctly reasoned that the vertical rocks had once been horizontal but were tilted and eroded off before deposition of the overlying horizontal rocks. Note the conglomerate at the boundary. *(From James Hutton, 1795, Theory of the Earth.)*

Figure 3-18 An anticline. *(Drawing by Wendell Wilson.)*

Figure 3-19   Aerial view of an eroded anticline. *(Courtesy of D. A. Rahm.)*

not necessarily so; resistant beds in a syncline might, after a long period of erosion of adjacent softer beds, form the hard crest of a mountain. This has occurred in the Appalachians. Many, but certainly not all, anticlines and synclines are the result of mountain building, which is taken up later in this chapter.

Large-scale features resembling anticlines and synclines in some ways are called *domes* and *basins*. However, they are not the result of compressional forces but are due to broader-scale vertical movements which cause upwarps and downwarps. The weight of accumulating sediment may even be a factor in the downwarping. The Ozark Dome, which occupies southern Missouri and northern Arkansas, and the Michigan Basin, which encompasses the southern peninsula of Michigan, are representative examples (Figure 3-20). (Which rocks would be exposed at the center of an eroded dome—the oldest or youngest? At the center of a basin?)

Buried Surfaces of Erosion   Folding and uplift inevitably lead to the erosion of the folded beds. Younger layers of sediment are commonly deposited upon such erosional surfaces. This is precisely what Hutton observed and correctly interpreted (Figure 3-17). These buried surfaces of erosion which

Figure 3-20 Diagrammatic representations of geologic cross sections of the Ozark Dome and the Michigan Basin. Rock units are labeled from oldest (1) to youngest. Note that the rock units thin toward the center of the dome (because it was a relatively high area during deposition) and thicken toward the center of the basin (because it subsided during deposition).

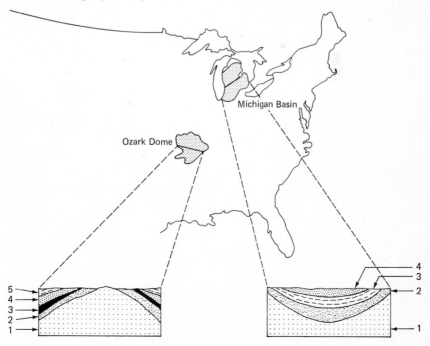

thus represent "missing rocks" are called *unconformities*. In special situations, an unconformity may represent nondeposition rather than erosion; such unconformities can be especially difficult to identify and require detailed studies of the fossils in the rocks above and below the unconformity in order to ascertain that a portion of geologic time is indeed not represented by rock.

The type described by Hutton is perhaps the easiest to recognize. Other kinds also exist (Figure 3-21). Regardless of the details, each unconformity records an episode of uplift and erosion, or nondeposition, and, when coupled with age information of the rocks both above and below the erosional surface, provides valuable insights into the detailed geological history of the region. In fact, interpretation of unconformities can indicate when folding and uplift occurred, how long the erosion lasted, and how much of the geological rock record has been removed by erosion or was not originally deposited.

If future seas were to cover much of the United States, the present exposed surface of the United States (which is currently a surface of erosion) would be buried beneath the new marine deposits. Thus, another unconformity would have been added to the rock record. Obviously, the new sediment would be deposited upon rocks of different ages and positions in different parts of the country. Its interpretation would be complicated but interesting

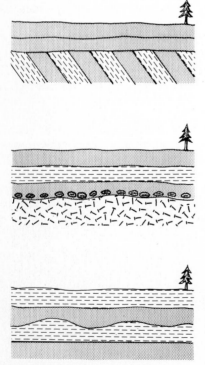

Figure 3-21 Three types of unconformities. The angular relationship in the top diagram is easy to recognize. The middle diagram represents sediments deposited upon weathered and eroded igneous or metamorphic rocks; note the pebbles of the underlying rock in the lowest sedimentary layer. The bottom diagram, with parallel beds above and below the unconformity, can be very difficult to recognize, especially if the unconformity is parallel to the bedding; fossil study is commonly necessary.

and revealing. (And wouldn't scientists of the distant future find an interesting array of fossils and artifacts scattered all over this unconformity?)

Faults   If pressure is applied relatively rapidly to rocks, especially near the earth's surface where the confining pressure and the temperature are low, most rocks will break rather than fold. The break occurs when the elastic limits of the rock are exceeded before the rock has had time to adjust to the new pressures. Conversely, stresses applied gradually over a longer period of time may cause the same rocks to fold rather than break.

The result of the pressures—whether compressional, owing to a squeezing together of part of the earth's crust, or extensional, owing to a "stretching," or extension, of the earth's crust—is a system of cracks called *joints*. [Some joints are the result of the cooling of magma or lava, for the solid rock occupies less space than the original molten rock (Figure 3-22). However, if you think about it, this is only a special case of an extensional type of stress.] If movement occurs along such a crack or joint, it becomes a fault.

The movement along a fault may be vertical, horizontal, or both. The nature of the stresses which caused the faulting can generally be determined

Figure 3-22   Devils Tower in northeastern Wyoming. Note the excellent columnar jointing due to the cooling of magma (*a*). The origin of Devils Tower is in some doubt; some geologists say it is a volcanic neck and others suggest it is an erosional remnant of a sill. Perhaps the sketch (*b*) is the best idea yet? It depicts a legend of the Kiowa tribe and was completed in 1936 by Herbert A. Collins. *(Courtesy of National Park Service.)*

(a)   (b)

by a study of the rocks on opposite sides of the faults. And faults are classified on the basis of the relative movement of the two sides. Fault zones are commonly good channels for the movement of ore-forming fluids, and consequently many mines are located along fault zones.

If the upper side of a dipping fault has gone down relative to the lower side, the fault is a *normal fault*, as in Figure 3-23. (Note that we said *relative* to the other side, for we see only the result of the movement. The actual movement could have involved the lower side's moving up, although this is not commonly the case.) Which type of stress—compressional or extensional—is likely to cause the upper side, or block, to move down relative to the lower side? Correct: extensional.

Conversely, if the upper side of a dipping fault moves up relative to the lower side, the fault is a *reverse fault* (Figure 3-23). Isn't it a compressional force which is most likely to cause the upper side to move upward over the lower side? Consequently, which type of fault is most likely to be associated with highly folded areas: normal or reverse?

Low-angle reverse faults are called *thrust faults* because the upper side is literally thrust up over and across the lower side. However, some thrust faults may be due to gravity sliding off a higher area. Thrust faults are nearly

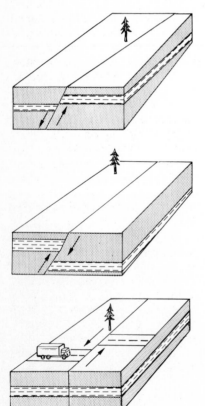

Figure 3-23 Three types of faults. The upper diagram shows a normal fault, the middle one a reverse fault, and the lower one a fault with only horizontal movement.

always found in mountain ranges where extreme folding has occurred. The rocks in the upper plates of many thrust faults have been moved tens of kilometers from their original locations. Obviously, great forces seem necessary to move such quantities of rock across such great distances. But the origin of such forces is not obvious.

Geologists have long believed that water along a thrust-fault plane acts as a lubricant, making movement easier. In 1959, geologists M. K. Hubbert and W. W. Rubey introduced a unique addition to the explanation. They suggested that water along the plane of a thrust fault was compressed by the weight of the overlying rock, and that the compressed water held up the slab of overlying rock, thereby minimizing friction of the slab against the underlying rock and permitting movement of rock along even gently dipping faults. They illustrated their theory with their infamous and elegant "beer can experiment." Upon a meter-long plate of glass, well cleaned so it would retain a film of water, they placed a beer can (previously emptied and open at one end) in an upright position. The glass plate had to be tilted to a 17° angle before the can would slide down. Then they chilled the can and placed it, open end upward, on the wetted glass plate; again it began to slide when the plate was tilted to a 17° angle. Finally, they rechilled the can, placed it open end *downward* on the wetted glass plate, this time tilted at only 1°. The can slid down the plate, stopping abruptly at the edge. Why? Hubbert and Rubey deduced that as the cold air in the inverted can expanded as it warmed, it increased the pressure in the can, and this helped support the weight of the can, thereby allowing it to slide more easily. The can stopped at the edge because the pressure of the fluid (in this case, air) was released as soon as part of the can moved over the edge of the glass. The geological implication of this nongeological experiment is that the pressure of the fluid (in this case, water) in the pores (open spaces) of rocks, when compressed during deformation of the rocks, is raised and can lift up, or "float," overlying thick slabs of rock. Thus, great slabs of rock, when given a push by deformation or a pull downslope by gravity, can be moved *without* tremendous forces being required. (Genius may be revealed in strange ways.)

Faults with horizontal movement are caused by horizontal forces acting toward each other but not along the same line, thus allowing for a lateral slipping of one block past another (Figure 3-23). Our best-studied example is the San Andreas fault in California (Figure 3-11). The side west of the fault, according to some geologists, may have moved northward relative to the rest of North America as much as 560 kilometers in the past 150 million years; evidence for this is some tenuous matching of rock units across the fault. At this rate, another 150 million years or so could find Los Angeles, which is west of the fault, and San Francisco, which is largely east of the fault, located side by side. This would surely cause Pacific Airlines stock to drop in value. (See how easily scientific data can be applied to other things? As Mark Twain said in *Life on the Mississippi*, "There is something fascinating about science. One gets such wholesome returns of conjecture out of such a trifling investment of fact.")

The San Andreas is well known to all Californians, for the two large metropolitan areas of Los Angeles and San Francisco, as well as all points between and beyond, experience frequent earthquakes caused by slippage along the numerous fault planes of this great fault zone.

MOUNTAIN BUILDING

There are several different kinds of mountains, but most can be classified into four main types—volcanic, fault-block, domal, and fold-belt. *Volcanic mountains* are perhaps the easiest to visualize; the big composite cones such as Mount Fuji and Mount Rainier are examples (Figure 3-1). A few mountain ranges, such as the Absarokas of Wyoming, are the result of the erosion of thick sequences of layered volcanic rocks. *Fault-block mountains*, such as the Grand Tetons of Wyoming (Figure 3-24), the Wasatch Range of Utah, and several dozens of smaller ranges in the Basin and Range province of the Southwestern United States, are the result of vertical movement along large normal faults. The Sierra Nevada ("Snowy Range") of California, the longest, highest, and grandest single mountain range in the adjacent 48 states, while having had a complex history, is presently an excellent example of a fault-block mountain. *Domal mountains* are exemplified by the Black Hills of South Dakota and the Adirondacks of New York; the rocks in these areas have been simply pushed upward, or domed, by pressures from below, and then eroded.

We still haven't mentioned the big mountain ranges of the world: The Alps, Himalayas, Andes, Appalachians, Atlas, and Rockies. They can all be classed as *fold-belt mountains*, a type that has a complex history. Several

Figure 3-24   The Grand Tetons of Wyoming. The steep eastern face, shown in the photo, is the result of a large normal fault dipping towards the east (lower right) with about 6000 meters of movement. The western face, not visible here, is a gentle slope because of tilting. The rugged topography of the range is the result of erosion, largely by glaciers. The topography in the foreground was sculpted by running water.

features are characteristic of most fold-belt mountains: a thick pile of faulted and folded sedimentary rocks, granitic batholiths, metamorphism, and roots beneath. The origins of fold-belt mountains will take us right into the last part of this chapter: continental drift and plate tectonic theory.

Geosynclinal Theory James Hall, the New York State Geologist in the mid-1800s, realized that the sedimentary rocks of the New York portion of the Appalachians were extremely thick compared with the sedimentary rock sequence farther to the west in western New York. This was the start of *geosynclinal theory*, the idea that certain long and narrow downwarped portions of the crust (later named *geosynclines*) received more sediment than more stable parts of the crust, and were finally uplifted to form fold-belt mountain ranges. This concept is of special interest to American geologists, for it probably was the first really important geologic concept advanced by geologists of the New World. European geologists, especially those working in the Alps, soon embellished the theory.

The geosyncline idea also provided a classic analogy to the argument of "which came first—the chicken or the egg?" Was there initially an elongated weak zone in the crust which subsided and then, because it was low, received a lot of marine sediment, or did the area receive a lot of sediment and then subside or sink under the weight? The former viewpoint now prevails.

Geologists soon realized that North America was once bounded by two major geosynclines: the Cordilleran in western North America and now uplifted into the Rocky Mountains, the Sierra Nevada, and other ranges; and the Appalachian geosyncline in the eastern part of the continent on the site of the Appalachian Mountains. Geosynclinal theory in North America reached a peak with the publication in 1949 of a book by Dr. Marshall Kay of Columbia University entitled *Geosynclines*. He showed that a classic geosyncline on the edge of a continent, such as the Appalachian geosyncline, was divided into two parts: a *miogeosyncline*, nearer the continent and containing sediments (sandstones, limestones, and shales) similar to but thicker than those on the more stable continent, and a *eugeosyncline*, seaward of the miogeosyncline and containing a different rock assemblage including pillowed basalts, bedded cherts, graded graywacke sandstones, and mudstones (Figure 3-25). The annual "Pick and Hammer Show" put on by geologists of the United States Geological Survey in Washington, D.C., had been blessed with another geologist upon whom they could pick and hammer. Lines such as "my geosyncline" and "your geosyncline" were quickly incorporated into their next skit.

Why are the geosynclinal rocks, and especially those of the eugeosyncline, later deformed, intruded by granitic batholiths, metamorphosed, and uplifted to form mountain ranges? This has long been a puzzle to geologists. The search for the ultimate cause has resulted in a number of theories for such mountain building on the sites of geosynclines.

Why Fold-Belt Mountains? It has been suggested that the lower part of the thick pile of geosynclinal sediments (commonly as thick as 16 kilometers) is depressed to a level in the crust which is very hot. Melting of these

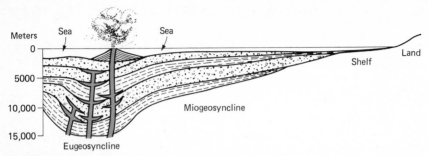

Figure 3-25 Idealized diagrammatic representation of a geosyncline with its two parts, the miogeosyncline and the eugeosyncline. Note that the sediments thicken from the shelf to the miogeosyncline to the eugeosyncline. The latter contains volcanic rocks (dark-colored), including pillowed lava flows and pyroclastic sedimentary rocks.

sedimentary rocks can occur at that depth, and, especially when molten, their lesser density compared to the surrounding rocks helps the new magmas as well as the deformed sedimentary rocks to rise.

It has also been suggested that the earth is cooling, and therefore shrinking, with the cooler outer crust buckling up as the inner parts of the earth continue to cool and shrink. But if so, shouldn't mountains be rather randomly distributed like the wrinkles on a dried-up prune or orange? And, the earth may not be cooling even though it is giving off small amounts of heat from within.

Another idea was based on continental drift: as the Americas drifted westward, the forward edge buckled, thus forming the Andes and the Rockies. But can this explain the Appalachians?

Still another explanation was based on convection-cell theory. A pair of downward-moving convection cells caused by heat transfer in the mantle might cause a sag in the overlying crust which would then fill with sediment. When the convection stopped, the then-filled sag would rise to form a mountain range.

A more recent theory is that of phase change: in the vicinity of the Moho, the elements present can change phase from basalt (density about 3.0 and composed of plagioclase, pyroxene, and olivine) to the rock eclogite (density about 3.3 and composed of pyroxene and garnet). The elements present haven't changed, nor have their amounts, but they've combined into less dense and more dense minerals, depending upon the pressure and temperature. The accompanying volume decrease when basalt changes to eclogite could cause a sag in the overlying crust, and when the change is from eclogite back to basalt, the volume increase would cause the then-filled sag to be raised higher than it was originally. These phase changes have been accomplished in the laboratory.

Other ideas on the origin of mountains have also been proposed. One farfetched one has huge slabs of rock from outer space hitting a still-molten earth, sticking in the magma, and standing up as mountains. This idea, actually published by a nongeologist, has absolutely no evidence to back it up.

Each of these theories has its problems. A very new theory—plate tectonic theory—apparently provides the best answers, as we shall see a few pages hence.

CONTINENTAL DRIFT

Perhaps even as a child in grade school, you noticed that the coastlines of South America and Africa appear to match up if placed next to each other (Figure 1-8). Way back in the early 1600s, when the first reasonable maps of the world appeared, Sir Francis Bacon of England had similar thoughts. In the 1850s, an American, Antonio Snider, suggested that the continents had separated during the Deluge; his book has "before" and "after" engravings of the globe.

The idea didn't really receive much attention, however, until 1915, when Alfred Wegener, a German, wrote a book entitled *The Origin of Continents and Oceans*. He amassed many lines of circumstantial evidence that the continents had once been together, even including the duplication of garden snail species on both sides of the Atlantic. In essence, he stated that the Atlantic Ocean did not exist 200 million years ago, but formed when an ancient supercontinent, which he named *Pangaea* (Greek for "all the earth"), broke apart.

This spurt of interest in the topic culminated in 1928 with an International Symposium on Continental Drift in New York; 14 papers were presented, of which 5 were for the idea, 2 were for it "with reservations," and 7 were against it. In general, the theory died for lack of a suitable mechanism to move the continents (Wegener suggested the mechanism as "earth tides" caused by the sun and moon), and when Wegener vanished in Greenland on a meteorological expedition in 1930, its main standard-bearer died, too.

Only geologists from the Southern Hemisphere, particularly some South African geologists, continued to support the theory, saying that they needed South America adjacent to Africa in order to explain the geology. They showed that not only do the continents match like pieces of a torn newspaper, but also the lines of "print" (the mountain ranges, rock types, and geologic structures) match. Furthermore, the "print" younger than Jurassic (130 million or so years ago) does not match, indicating that the continents were torn apart at about that point in the earth's history.

What was the evidence for drift? It was varied; in addition to the matching coastlines, the mountains, the rocks, and the fossils, it included much paleoclimatic evidence. Ancient glacial deposits (*tillites*) and glacially scratched pavement beneath the tillites occur in the southern continents, and if these continents were reassembled, a picture would emerge of glaciers radiating outward about 255 to 340 million years (m.y.) ago from the central portion of a single, large, composite southern continent, dubbed *Gondwanaland* (Figure 3-26). And while this glaciation was going on in the Southern Hemisphere, coal was forming in subtropical portions of the Northern Hemisphere. Also, a number of fossil plants called the *Glossopteris* flora

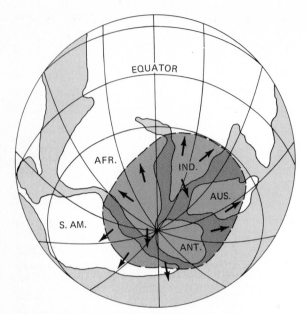

Figure 3-26   Gondwanaland and the large area glaciated sometime between 255 and 340 m.y. ago. Note arrows showing glacial movement.

appear above the glacial deposits in the rock record of all the southern continents. Presumably they could not have spread without the existence of one large landmass or, alternatively, land bridges spanning the oceans between continents. Such evidence continues to accumulate: within the past decade, bones of the same species of a primitive ancient reptile, *Lystro-saurus*, have been found in Antarctica and in Africa.

The opponents and proponents were emphatic with respect to continental drift. In contrast to the stance of the South Africans, a 1959 edition of a much-used American advanced geology text included the short statement that the idea is "outrageous, of course." But all arguments, both pro and con, were based largely upon the geology of only the exposed 30 percent of the earth's surface area—the continents. Since the early 1940s, scientists have compounded their knowledge of the ocean floors time and time again. And therein, there in the ocean basins, lie the keys to the hidden secrets.

PLATE TECTONICS
Plate tectonic theory sounds pretty imposing. The word *tectonic* simply refers to the deformation of earth materials on a large scale. A *plate* is a large piece of the lithosphere, as we will see shortly. *Theory*, of course, indicates that we "know" the concept is true but that ultimate proof is lacking.

Ocean-Floor Topography   Oceanographic studies of the last two decades have led to a number of surprising discoveries. The ocean floor, rather than being quite flat as long suspected, is highly irregular. The features described in Chapter 1, especially the midoceanic ridges of the Atlantic and Indian Oceans and the off-center ridge of the Pacific, are of special interest (Figures 1-8 and 1-9).

The ridge system, all connected, is more than 65,000 kilometers long. The best-studied ridge, the Mid-Atlantic Ridge, is as much as 2400 kilometers wide and rises more than 3 kilometers from the adjacent abyssal plains. A down-dropped rift valley as much as 2.5 kilometers deep and 32 to 48 kilometers wide extends down its crest. Isn't faulting the most obvious explanation for such down-dropped valleys with steep, parallel, and stepped sides? The abundance of earthquake epicenters in a narrow zone along the ridge crest supports this conclusion. Volcanism is common along the ridge, and much heat is being released along this zone. All these data are, as we'll see shortly, highly significant in the big earth picture.

Equally important to the big picture is the distribution of the deep-sea trenches (Figure 1-7), which are hundreds of kilometers long, tens of kilometers wide, and 6000 to 11,000 meters deep. The trenches are seismically very active: about 80 percent of the world's shallow earthquakes occur near the trenches, and more than 90 percent of the deeper earthquakes occur adjacent to the trenches on their landward sides. We've already seen that earthquakes are due to faulting. Therefore, what's the suggested relationship here?

And the matching continental outlines, which helped trigger the entire idea, were found to match even better than before. Computer plots of South America and Africa, utilizing the true edges of the continents (the bases of the slopes), show an amazingly good fit. North America, Africa, and Europe also tuck together pretty well (Figure 3-27).

Paleomagnetism and Sea-Floor Spreading   Iron-bearing minerals, especially those crystallizing from lavas, are affected by the earth's geomagnetic field. They align themselves in this field and point north, much like a compass needle does. Therefore, geologists can collect oriented rock samples in the field, take them back to the laboratory, and by means of special instruments determine the orientation of the earth's magnetic field at the time the rock was formed. These measurements thus give the position of the paleomagnetic north pole at the time the rocks were formed.

A plot of pole positions of North American rocks of different geological ages shows that the magnetic north pole has been "wandering" through time. It was once located out in the Pacific Ocean beyond Los Angeles, but it slowly migrated across the Pacific into Siberia, and then looped northward to its present position nearer to the geographic pole. And when the magnetic north pole positions as determined by analyses of rocks from the other continents are plotted, the positions do *not* coincide with the poles determined for North American rocks. If the pole positions of a given time were the same for all continents, it would mean simply that the pole had wandered. However, the different pole positions strongly suggest that not only has the pole wandered, but also the continents have been moving relative to each other. India has done the most traveling of the wanderers. It was this

Figure 3-27 Computer fit of North America, South America, Africa, and Europe. *(After Konrad B. Kranskopf and Arthur Beiser, 1971, Fundamentals of Physical Science, McGraw-Hill.)*

paleomagnetic evidence which was a major factor in the renewal of the question of continental drift and has made the argument of continental-scale movements respectable.

Another form of paleomagnetic evidence has been instrumental in the latest theories. Aeromagnetic surveys over the Mid-Atlantic Ridge showed that the magnetism of the rocks on the sea floor form a symmetrical pattern of strips parallel to the ridge, and that the strips on opposite sides of the ridge can be matched up. The same patterns were found elsewhere along oceanic ridges (Figure 3-28). The strips are alternating bands of basalt of "normal" polarity with the north pole to the north and bands of "reversed" polarity with the north pole toward the south. Very detailed comparisons with rocks on land which also show these reversals and which can be radiometrically age-dated as well have shown that the matching strips on opposite sides of the ridge are in rocks of equal ages. Furthermore, the rocks are young near the ridge and become successively older away from the ridge; the ages of fossils dredged from the sea floor add further support.

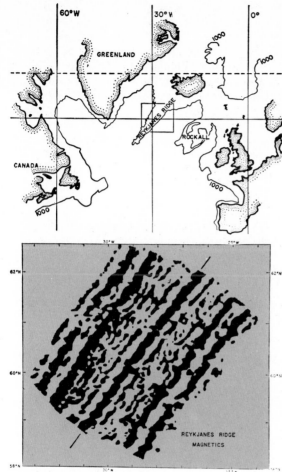

Figure 3-28 Striped magnetic patterns flanking both sides of the Mid-Atlantic Ridge southwest of Iceland. This was first mapped in the early 1960s. Note that the strips are parallel to the ridge axis and that each strip can be matched with one on the other side of the ridge. *(Courtesy of J. R. Heirtzler et al., 1966, by permission of Deep Sea Research, Pergamon Press, Ltd.)*

There have been 171 reversals of the polarity in the past 76 m.y., with an "average" normal interval of 420,000 years and an "average" reversed interval of 480,000 years. The present normal era has lasted 700,000 years, suggesting to some "paleomagicians" that we are already overdue for a reversal. In fact, the strength of the earth's magnetic field has decreased 6 percent in the last 100 years, and perhaps 50 percent in the last 2500 years. Presumably the earth's magnetic field diminishes to a very low strength, and when it builds up again, it is reversed.

Why reversals? We think that the earth's magnetic field is generated by eddies in the fluid outer core, as mentioned in Chapter 1. Changes in the flow pattern could cause reversals. Allen Cox, one of the leading workers in the field, stated that "the earth is operating as a bi-stable flip-flop circuit." (Now do you understand?) Whether the flip-flop is due to changes in the earth's internal "dynamo" or to external causes such as large meteorites hitting the earth is not yet known for sure, but the causes seem likely to be internal.

Such reversed and normal magnetic strips are found adjacent to all the oceanic ridges. Whatever the mysterious origin of the reversals, the reversals allow us to calculate rates of spread of the ocean floor. The increasing ages of the rocks away from the ridges can hardly lead to any interpretation other than that new oceanic crust is being formed at the ridge centers. The basaltic volcanism along the ridges—the Azores and Iceland, for example, are on the Mid-Atlantic Ridge—supports this conclusion. The records of magnetic reversal show that the separation rate is highest in the southeast Pacific (15 to 20 centimeters per year) and is only 2 to 5 centimeters per year in the Atlantic. (At this rate, how long ago was the 2400-kilometer-wide Atlantic Ocean nonexistent, with the Eastern and Western Hemispheres part of the same landmass?)

A Mechanism The mechanism for moving continents, which Wegener and other early proponents lacked, has now been proposed; slow-moving convection currents in the earth's mantle. Heat is generated within the earth by radioactive decay, the heated rock material expands and rises toward the surface, and then, as it cools off near the surface, it again descends. Thus, convection cells are developed in the mantle as a result of heat flow, somewhat as heating water in a pot moves up and then down in a closed pattern or cycle.

But how can anyone prove that such convection cells do exist? Unfortunately, no one can. We can only make models, and the convection-cell model appears to fit the data.

The Plate-Tectonics Model Integration of all these lines of evidence has led scientists to a global model in which the lithosphere consists of six major *plates* and several smaller ones, each moving relative to the other plates (Figure 3-29). Each plate is in reality a rigid cap on the spherical earth surface. Each plate consists of rigid lithosphere including the crust and some upper mantle, totaling 80 to 150 kilometers in thickness. The plates rest on the hot rock material of the asthenosphere, the low-velocity zone near the upper boundary of the mantle, and it is this weak zone which allows the overlying plates to move as the asthenosphere "flows" in response to upwelling convection currents.

As the rigid plates are moving relative to one another, the boundaries between the moving plates are the critical areas. Three types of relative movement at these boundaries seem logical on a mechanical basis, and indeed all boundaries appear to be one of these types: (1) *divergent* boundaries, where two plates are moving away from each other, (2) *convergent* boundaries, where two plates are moving toward each other, and (3) *lateral-motion* boundaries, where two plates are sliding past each other with a horizontal movement. The plates are moving as if on gigantic conveyor belts.

Divergent plate boundaries are the oceanic ridges along which sea-floor spreading is occurring (Figures 1-8 and 1-9). Here new oceanic crust is being

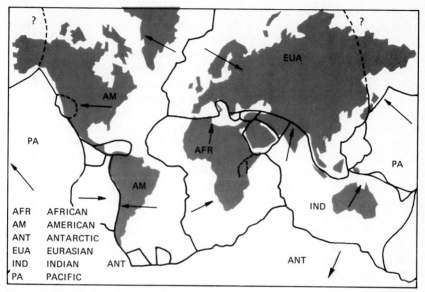

Figure 3-29 Plates of the earth's crust. Arrows indicate relative movement. *(After Konrad B. Krauskopf and Arthur Beiser, 1971, Fundamentals of Physical Science, McGraw-Hill.)*

formed as the two plates move away from each other. Basaltic magma steadily rises from below to "fill the gap"; actually, of course, no real gap can exist. Volcanism, generally subsea but in some places above the water surface as well, attests to this process. Presumably the magmas originate by a partial melting of the upper mantle beneath the plate junction. Apparently all oceanic crust was formed in this way. The subsequent movement of the young rock units near the spread boundaries makes the ridges zones of earthquake activity as well as zones of volcanism.

Convergent plate boundaries are boundaries along which crust must be consumed in order for the earth to maintain a constant size. This consumption occurs by *subduction*, the process by which a denser (basaltic) oceanic plate sinks beneath a lighter (granitic) continental plate and is eventually recycled into the underlying mantle. This subduction readily explains the lack of old oceanic crust. Whereas geologists once thought they would find in the ocean basins a complete sedimentary record of the world since its beginning, no rocks older than about 200 m.y. have been found on the ocean floors.

The tops of the subduction zones are expressed on the ocean floors as trenches. Some are apparently devoid of sediment, whereas others such as the Puerto Rican trench and part of the Chilean trench contain much sediment.

Convergent plate boundaries are similar to the divergent boundaries in that they are also zones of volcanic and earthquake activity. The volcanism is, however, of a different nature. The lavas are not just basaltic as along the ridges, but include a variety of volcanic compositions; andesite, of a composition intermediate between mafic (basaltic) and felsic (granitic) rocks, is the most common rock type. The andesitic magmas may be in part due to partial melting of the descending plate of basalt and oceanic sediments, or may be in part due to the partial melting of upper mantle.

The volcanism results in the many spectacular volcanic island arcs of the Pacific Ocean Basin such as Japan, the Philippines, and the Aleutians. More rarely, the volcanic arc is on a continent; the Andes are our prime example. Together, these volcanic zones make up the Ring of Fire around the Pacific. A few arcs occur in other parts of the world.

The subduction zones are also the sites of most of the world's earthquakes. The shallow ones are in the vicinity of the trenches, and the deeper ones are beneath the volcanic arcs; thus they locate the positions of the descending plates at depth. Figure 3-30 illustrates a subduction zone.

A close study of Figure 3-29 will show that convergent plate boundaries may consist of oceanic crust against oceanic crust or oceanic crust against continental crust. In both cases, subduction occurs. A third situation can also occur with continental crust meeting continental crust; we will come back to this a few paragraphs hence.

Lateral-motion plate boundaries involve horizontal movement with no material being consumed or created. The best-studied plate boundary of this type is in California—the San Andreas fault zone—which we have already mentioned because of its numerous earthquakes. Note from Figures 1-8 and

Figure 3-30 Model of subduction zone, where a heavy oceanic plate meets a lighter continental plate. Magmas form at depth and rise to create a volcanic arc, either as an island arc or on a continent. Note sediment accumulating in trench, deformed rocks near the boundary of the two plates, the location of earthquakes (*X*'s) beneath volcanic arc and rising bodies of magma from the zone of partial melting.

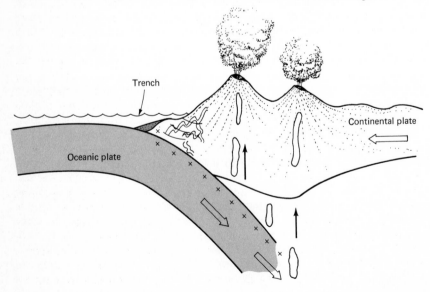

Trench

Continental plate

Oceanic plate

3-29 that North America has overridden the east Pacific spread boundary. The direction of movement of the Pacific plate in the north Pacific Ocean is to the northwest, and the direction of movement of the American plate is more westerly but at a slower rate. The combination of these two forces has resulted in this lateral-motion fault boundary, the San Andreas fault zone, along which the land west of the fault is moving northwestward at a rate of about 2 centimenters per year. Consequently, the slippage causes frequent earthquakes. As these are all shallow earthquakes not related to a present subduction zone, the energy is dissipated near the surface and can cause extensive damage.

Mountain Building (Again) Convergent plate boundaries are also the sites of the world's major fold-belt mountain ranges. Evidently subduction is accompanied by deformation (including folding and thrust faulting), the intrusion of batholiths, metamorphism, and uplift. The Andes chain is an example of a still-growing mountain range related to a subduction zone.

The Alps and the Himalayas, two of the largest mountain ranges in the world, are the result of converging plates, but of a somewhat special case in which continental crust of one plate collided with continental crust of another plate. Continental material is too light to be subducted down into the asthenosphere, and so in the process of convergence, the crustal layer becomes abnormally thick. Thus, the Indian subplate and the African plate collided with the Eurasian plate, forming the Himalayas-Tibetan Plateau and the Alps, respectively. Presumably the Appalachians had a similar origin when older African, European, and North American continental plates collided.

The mountains of westernmost North America, the Coast Ranges and the Sierra Nevada, can be related to subduction zones which ceased to exist when North America overrode the divergent plate boundary of the eastern Pacific (Figure 3-29), and the San Andreas fault boundary developed. Much of the complexity in the geology of western North America may be related to the effect of North America's passing over this plate boundary. However, the Rocky Mountains of the western interior pose somewhat of a problem. Their origin has not yet been satisfactorily explained by plate tectonic theory.

With these new insights into mountain building, is the geosynclinal theory outmoded? Some geologists prefer to discard geosynclinal theory, but others think that it can, with modifications, be meshed with plate tectonic theory. That is, the geosynclines are closely related to convergent plate boundaries. The thick sediments which accumulate seaward of the volcanic arcs may be the miogeosynclinal deposits, and the sediments which accumulate in the trenches, and which are later mixed with pillowed basalts and chert skimmed off the subducting oceanic plates, may comprise the eugeosynclinal assemblage. Thick subsea fans are collecting at the bases of many of the continental slopes of the world—perhaps they are geosynclines? Quite possibly the weights of these thick prisms could eventually initiate subduction where none is going on today. The compression of the subduction zones can explain the deformation, and the batholiths occur as bodies of plutonic rock intrusive into the closely related volcanic arc rocks. The crust under Japan is of continental rather than oceanic thickness, and this is akin to mountain roots; in this way, volcanic arcs are contributing to the growth of continents.

Some geologists attribute many of the copper and associated ore deposits (Figure 2-34) of plutons and volcanic accumulations to origins in oceanic crust with later concentration by partial melting of this crust along subduction zones. Maps showing locations of ore deposits strengthen this suggestion.

Against Plate Tectonic Theory Whereas most earth scientists, even some who were originally vehemently opposed to the outrageous idea of continental drift, have jumped aboard the plate-tectonics bandwagon, not everyone is enamored with the theory. These few doubting scientists are urging caution in applying this concept to the explanation of so many geological processes and features.

For example, the opponents say that the paleomagnetic data can be interpreted differently (perhaps the earth had not only two poles but four) and that the scatter in the plots of pole positions for rocks of a given age is greater in area than the entire Atlantic Ocean. Some dispute the paleoclimatic evidence, saying the planetary wind and ocean-current circulation patterns have changed little in the past 1 billion years, and that this stability necessitates the continued location of the earth's rotational pole, ocean basins, and continents in the same places for the last billion years. In other words, the poles may have moved but not the continents. They also point out that convection cells are not well-substantiated as a mechanism.

S. W. Carey of Tasmania has long been a proponent of an expanding earth, whereas most scientists say its size has not changed appreciably. He suggests an expansion of the earth's total surface area by 76 percent, or a 33 percent increase in radius, in the past 200 million years. If this is accurate, then subduction is not necessary to eliminate an area of crust at the convergent plate boundaries equal to that being formed at the divergent plate boundaries. He adds that the oceanic trenches are normal fault zones and are the result of extension rather than compression.

Some readers might agree with the opponents of plate tectonics, saying that the whole idea of moving plates, or continents, is impossible anyway. But we must bear in mind the scale of the earth. It seems solid to us because of our small size relative to its radius of 6370 kilometers. But if the earth were scaled down to a globe less than 1 meter in diameter, with *all* properties scaled down accordingly, the earth would have the consistency of soft mud and wouldn't even retain its shape if set on the floor.

Concluding Statement You may have noted that continental drift has hardly been mentioned in this section on plate tectonics. True, it was the grandfather of plate tectonic theory. However, the continents are but passive passengers on top of the much thicker plates, which are so broad as to include oceanic crust as well as continental crust. Therefore, *continental* *drift*, which implies free-drifting individual continents, is now a somewhat obsolete term.

While plate tectonics is still a theory and may well always remain so, because direct verification of what is occurring at depth within the earth is impossible, it is certainly a grand unifying theory which appears to explain large-scale earth features and processes, including much volcanism, earthquakes, large-scale horizontal faulting, and mountain building. It is certainly one of the greatest theories since evolution was so eloquently stated by Darwin in his *On the Origin of Species* in 1859.

The present plates are continuing to move today, after having started on their journeys about 225 m.y. ago with the breakup of Pangaea. We have already noted that the Appalachians may have formed during an earlier cycle of plate motions. How far back into the distant pages of earth's history can plate tectonics be pushed? Some geologists are suggesting that volcanic rocks 2.7 billion years old may have formed in volcanic arcs over subduction zones. Evidence for such ancient events is hard to come by.

What does the future hold as a result of the continuing plate motion? A look at the relative motions shown in Figure 3-29 will suggest that eventually the Atlantic will be the big ocean and that the Pacific will be small. Some scientists think that the Gulf of California and the Red Sea will be the ocean basins of the future. The Mediterranean may be closed up completely as Africa pushes northward against Europe. But don't lose too much sleep over these predictions; it will be a long time before their fulfillment.

Plate tectonic theory is, in detail, extremely complex. Mathematical solutions to plate movements involve spherical geometry, for the earth's surface is not planar. This chapter has merely highlighted the main aspects of the concept, and in so doing, has certainly oversimplified it in several places. The authors of this text encourage you to read other texts on the subject, especially a companion volume in this series, by John Bird and Karen Goodman. It and other references are listed at the end of the book.

Is this theoretical, scientific, and academic stuff about plates relevant to modern-day living? Yes, it may be relevant in at least one very practical way. It has been seriously proposed that people package the great volumes of waste and litter which they generate and which they have difficulty subduing, and drop the packages into the oceanic trenches, where subduction will ultimately dispose of it. That would be recycling on a global scale.

FOUR

EARTH'S SURFACE PROCESSES AND EFFECTS

The previous chapter should have imparted to you the idea that, internally, the earth is a restless, ever-changing planet. Continents moving, rocks deforming, mountains rising—none of these commonplace events normally occurs with enough speed to make itself evident to the senses. The occasional earthquake or volcanic eruption, however, very quickly impresses upon those close by that something is going on. The geologic processes occurring at the earth's surface, in contrast, usually are fairly rapid in rate, but in spite of that and their omnipresence they too most often operate without much awareness of the ordinary bystander. And why not? After all, the surface environment is where we evolved and live, and familiarity does breed a degree of contempt. One rainstorm on the moon would shake the scientific world, but one here might only cause the shake of a golfer's head in irritation. Nonetheless, surficial geologic processes are largely responsible for such planetary-scale phenomena as the shape of the land, the concentrations of many economically important minerals, the ionic composition of seawater and, probably most directly important to humans, the formation of soil. These processes can be very complex and intertwined. To facilitate an understanding of basic concepts of surficial geology, it is convenient to separate these interacting processes into *weathering, erosion*, and *deposition*.

WEATHERING

Although we generally look up to decide what the weather is, the weathering of rocks occurs at the land's surface and down into the earth as far as water, air, and temperature changes penetrate. This depth is usually only a few to a few hundred meters, and, geologically, the surface of earth is treated as a zone. The main pathway of penetration in nonporous rock is normally along cracks. Nearly all exposed bodies of rock have one or more sets of reasonably parallel fractures, or *joints*, running through them. These fractures are not faults, for no significant movement along the fractures has occurred. Joints are commonly produced during a volume loss either as an igneous body cools and shrinks or as sediments lose water during lithification. Also, crustal forces may cause rock bodies to move or undergo stress with sufficient rapidity to fracture. One type of joint pattern seems to reflect surficial conditions and can be treated along with weathering processes; if rock that was buried deeply, especially an igneous body that formed at depth, is uplifted and uncovered, the relief of pressure results in expansion and fracturing. This type of joint production results in a pattern of fractures that tends to parallel the topography (Figure 4-1). Joints produced by other means usually have little relation to the land surface and often exhibit two or more sets of joints with different orientations (Figure 4-2).

Were you more closely to examine an exposure of igneous rock, say granite, the fact that the rock is breaking down often would be evident. The presence of relatively small pieces broken off the parent mass would be one criterion and, especially on the more horizontal surfaces of the main rock body, that some of the minerals between the quartz grains had altered and

Figure 4-1   Joints subparallel to topography. *(Courtesy of United States Geological Survey; photo by B. K. Gilbert.)*

Figure 4-2 Two sets of joints in an igneous rock. Note how weathering, initially at quite sharp corners where joints intersect, is rounding the pieces.

softened would be another. *Weathering is the physical and chemical break-down (in place) of rock material.*

Physical Weathering Physical weathering, sometimes referred to as me-chanical weathering or disintegration, is simply the fracturing of rock into smaller pieces. No change in composition occurs, nor do chemical reactions take place.

Pressure is the most basic factor in physical weathering. As mentioned above, joints formed by pressure relief are a cause of physical disintegration of rock. There are other ways that pressure can fracture rock, and the most important is a process known as *frost action*. Frost action occurs in colder climates seasonally but is most effective at high elevations where freezing and thawing may occur daily. Water expands in volume about 9 percent when it freezes. In water-filled cracks and crevasses in rock, the water at the surface freezes first as the temperature drops and the initial ice layers effectively confine the still-liquid water below. As more liquid water becomes ice, the increasing volume exerts considerable force on the confining rock. Repetitive action eventually causes pieces of rock to become loose, and in mountainous areas the slopes are often littered with angular fragments of rock (Figure 4-3).

Porous rocks, such as many sandstones, are very effectively weathered by frost action. When water occupying pore spaces between sand grains freezes and expands, grains are loosened and finally freed. If you want your tombstone to last, specify a nonporous rock.

Rock outcrops in hot deserts may be surrounded by angular broken-off fragments, yet no appreciable water seems available for frost action. Since temperatures on rock surfaces may vary some 70°C between day and night, it is thought this might be enough to fracture rocks. The idea of *thermal expansion and contraction* became somewhat controversial when laboratory experiments simulating such changes every 15 minutes for the equivalent of 2 centuries produced no noticeable change in the rock samples. Since an area now desert may have had a much different climate in the past, frost action could have produced some of this. However, it is not likely, given the prevalence of this fragmentation in so many deserts, that a past climate is always the answer. Perhaps a bit of dew enters the process, or more likely, it simply requires thousands—not hundreds—of years to do the job.

Organic activity also contributes to the physical breakdown of rock. Plant roots entering small cracks will wedge rock apart as the plant grows, and human beings certainly enter the scene with quarrying, mining, and road building.

THE EFFECT OF PHYSICAL WEATHERING The principal result of physical weathering is the production of surfaces. Increased surface area causes the rate of chemical weathering to be far greater than otherwise. The effect of rock fracture on surface area can be appreciated easily if you consider the following: A block of rock 1 meter on each side has a total surface area open to chemical action of 6 square meters (Figure 4-4). Fracturing the rock through each face, separating it into 8 blocks each with 1.5 square meters of

Figure 4-3 Frost action. Angular pieces of rock fragmented from the main rock mass by repeated freezing and thawing of water in cracks. *(Courtesy of C. L. Matsch.)*

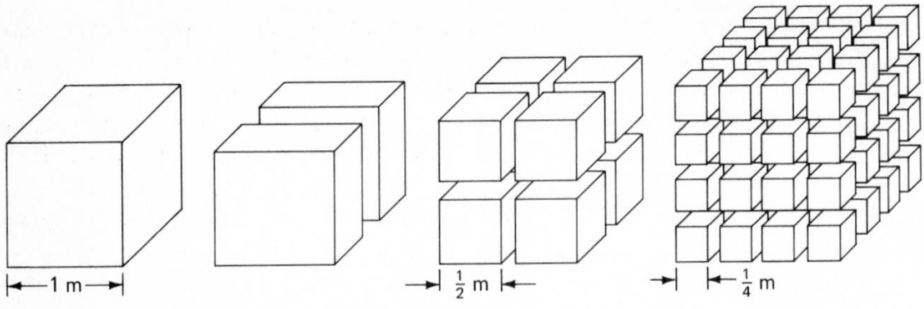

|←—1 m—→| →| ½ m |←   →| |← ¼ m

(a)   (b)   (c)   (d)

Figure 4-4 The increase in surface area, and therefore in the rate of chemical weathering, as a result of jointing or other fracturing. The 1-meter cube of rock (a) with a surface area of 6 square meters will have doubled in area when fractured into 8 cubes (c).

surface area, results in a doubling of the original total surface area to 12 square meters. Very effective, and one can easily imagine what further disintegration by frost action or other processes can do to increase the rate of chemical weathering and ultimately lead to the disappearance of the rock.

Chemical Weathering The most important factors influencing the rate of chemical breakdown of rock are as follows: (1) surface area—the more area available for reaction, the higher the rate; (2) climate—the wetter the climate, the faster the rate; the warmer the climate, the faster the rate; and (3) composition—some minerals, therefore some types of rock, weather more rapidly than others.

Surface area as a factor needs no further explanation. Most chemical reactions proceed faster with the addition of heat, and so a warmer climate obviously facilitates chemical decomposition. When you realize that *water* is the principal reagent in chemical weathering, the fact that the rate of weathering is higher where water is abundant is not a startling revelation. Rock composition is not so obvious a factor, and a thorough review of this would get us back into chemical bonding and atomic lattice structure. The general concept is that, for igneous rocks, those that crystallize first weather first; the order is therefore essentially the same as Bowen's series of crystallization (Figure 2-13) and indicates that ferromagnesian minerals and calcium feldspars tend to weather more rapidly than, say, orthoclase or quartz. In essence, calcium feldspar crystallized under higher pressure and temperature conditions, farther from the conditions on the earth's surface, than orthoclase feldspar. The calcium feldspar is more "out of its environment" and is less stable. Therefore, a granite is more durable at the earth's surface than a gabbro. The rate of chemical decomposition is not directly related to hardness. The reason olivine ($H = 6.5$ to 6.7) is rare as a component of beach sand while quartz ($H = 7$) is so common is due to compositional and molecular-structural differences between the two minerals. Quartz is resistant to chemical reactions with water; olivine, less so.

Along with the chemically durable quartz, calcium carbonate (usually in the form of limestone) and clays (usually in shales) are the most abundant sedimentary-rock minerals. Clay, as we will discuss, is largely formed at the surface and is quite at home in that environment. It, too, is relatively resistant to chemical weathering. Of the three, calcium carbonate is the most easily weathered. One of the easiest ways to gain some appreciation of weathering rates of various rocks is to examine older tombstones. Those made of slate, with a high mica content, or granite retain their inscriptions longer than those made of marble. Their weathering differential may also be reflected in the topography of an area (Figure 4-5).

Most of the water that enters rock at the earth's surface is rainwater, and rainwater is not pure water. It contains not only variable quantities of ions but dissolved gases as well. Most rain tends to be somewhat acid in nature, principally because of carbon dioxide in the atmosphere. Additional carbon dioxide and other substances are normally added after it enters the surficial water system, further increasing its ability to weather rock. The principal reaction with the atmosphere may be shown by the equation

$$H_2O \ CO_2 \rightarrow H_2CO_3 \qquad \text{(carbonic acid)}$$

This weak acid can further ionize:

$$H_2CO_3 \rightleftharpoons H^+ + HCO_3^- \rightleftharpoons 2H^+ + CO_3^{2-}$$

How much of the various ions are present varies with temperature, pressure, amount of CO_2 in solution, and the presence or absence of other ions. The carbon dioxide–charged water will dissolve limestone, sometimes leading to the formation of caverns, by a process called *carbonation*:

$$\underset{\text{(limestone)}}{CaCO_3} + \underset{\text{(acidic water)}}{(H_2O + CO_2)} \rightarrow \underset{\text{(in solution)}}{Ca(HCO_3)_2}$$

Under ideal conditions a 1-centimeter rainfall can dissolve about 3 tons of limestone per square kilometer of surface. Since the industrial revolution the increased carbon dioxide added to our atmosphere by burning fossil fuels, mostly coal and oil, has increased the rate of chemical weathering. In some industrial areas the surface of limestone buildings and statues may visibly deteriorate during one's lifetime.

Sometimes changes in pressure or temperature permit less CO_2 to be in solution, and the equation may go in the opposite direction. This may lead to precipitation of limestone near hot springs or as stalactites and other structural forms in caverns (Figure 4-6).

The ionization of carbonic acid in rain-derived groundwaters makes hydrogen ions, H+, available. This active ion exchanges with the metallic ions present in common rock-forming minerals and leads to their chemical decomposition. Plants increase the reactiveness of groundwaters by adding additional CO_2 as well as organic acids. The concept of how an igneous rock, such as granite, is attacked and weathered chemically by water may be understood by following a simplified unbalanced equation. Consider that a

(a)

(b)

Figure 4-5 Differential weathering. The closeup photographs of tombstones in New England illustrate how slate (a) had weathered since 1842 compared to limestone (b) since 1846. (c) (opposite page) The different types of rocks weather at different rates and cause the rugged topography.

(c)

Figure 4-5 continued

Figure 4-6 A cavern in limestone, principally developed through solution by groundwater. Groundwater dripping from the ceiling has later caused the precipitation of
limestone in the form of numerous stalactites from the cave ceiling and a few
stalagmites on the cavern floor. *(Courtesy of Luray Caverns, Va.)*

granitic rock is composed of orthoclase feldspar, $KAlSi_3O_8$; a plagioclase feldspar, $(Ca,Na)Al_2Si_2O_8$; and quartz, SiO_2.

$$KAlSi_3O_8 + (H_2O + CO_2) \rightarrow KHCO_3 + H_4SiO_4 + Al_2Si_2O_5(OH)_4$$
$$\quad\quad\quad\quad\quad\quad\quad\quad\text{(solution)}\quad\text{(solution)}\quad\quad\text{(clay)}$$

The reactions are complex but the idea is easily appreciated and worth consideration. Note the three products: potassium (K) is now in solution, some of the silica (Si) is in solution, and the third formula is that of a clay, *not* in solution. Clay then has been *produced*, and ions have been put into solution in the earth's waters. Plagioclase undergoes a similar reaction, and calcium and sodium go into solution and more clay is formed.

The reaction of quartz with the CO_2-charged water can be summed up as "not much." Quartz, structurally resistant to weathering under most surficial conditions, tends only to be freed from granitic rocks, not altered.

What then, in general terms, does all this mean? It means that by these and other weathering reactions with water and atmosphere, rocks are broken down. The elevation of the land is lowered as weathering products are carried away, mainly by water, and the components of once solid rock are made available for many uses.

The Products of Weathering

IN SOLUTION   With time, the ions in a water solution may follow an uncountable number of pathways. Iron, once freed in small quantities from minerals, may be oxidized and deposited with various sediments. Many quartz sandstones, for example, are colored red owing to small quantities of oxidized iron. Prior to the existence of free oxygen in our atmosphere the freed iron accumulated in the seas. Apparently when free oxygen began to become present, this iron oxidized and formed concentrated deposits when it precipitated. Most of the world's iron ore is thought to have been produced in this way. Chapter 6 will develop this subject a bit further. Freed ions, such as iron, calcium, potassium, and sodium, have become essential to plants and animals. The whole history of organic evolution is linked directly to chemical weathering; for example, the calcium for shells and bones and the ions involved in nerve impulse transmission and in muscle reactions were all originally in rock. For billions of years, rivers have carried ions to the seas. The ions have afforded material for the growth of organisms in the oceans and have been concentrated there to form an important part of its saline nature. If the sea is the "mother of life" on this planet, surely chemical weathering is a blood relation.

SOLIDS   The clays that formed during the weathering processes are further weathered only under humid tropical conditions. There, silica may be removed and the aluminum concentrated as bauxite, the principal ore of the metal. More commonly, the clays may be transported and later deposited, resulting in shales. The clay itself has economic uses, for the manufacture of products ranging from cement to tea cups. To humans, clays are most essential since they help form fertile soils, but soil too often goes unappreciated as the most vital natural resource of most nations.

Quartz, now freed (originally from igneous rocks) as relatively small particles, forms the common sand of the earth. Its uses to humans are wide, for example, in the manufacture of both glass and concrete, so prevalent in modern cities. As a sedimentary rock, the spaces between grains provide pathways for the migration, and sites for the accumulation, of underground water and petroleum.

SOIL

Loose rock debris from weathering, either formed in place or transported and deposited away from its site of origin, is called *regolith*. When it can support rooted plants, it is called soil. As regolith becomes soil, further weathering supplemented by organic activity occurs. Still with water as the principal agent, elements migrate downward or upward through the clay, silt, and sand of common soils. Which ions migrate where is closely tied to the climate. In drier climates evaporation of surface waters may result in water rising upward through the soil, bringing salts in solution which precipitate near the surface. The calcium carbonate hardpan near the surface in more arid areas of North America formed this way. In humid regions the downward migrations of water carries clays and ions to lower levels. These actions will, in time, result in soil with a layered appearance. The succession of these soil *horizons* from the surface down to solid rock is known as the *soil profile* (Figure 4-7).

The depth of a soil profile is a function of time and climate. In an arid region the profile may be less than a meter in thickness, while in the humid tropics the weathering may extend down more than 100 meters. In a given climate one might imagine that soils formed in place over a parent rock would vary greatly according to the original mineralogy of the rock. This is true in the early stages, but as the soils develop a distinct profile, thereby becoming *mature* soils, they tend to have similar characteristics. Mature soils reflect the nature of their climatic region more than that of their parent material.

Soils have been classified in many ways, none of which were, or are, entirely satisfactory. With so much potential for variability according to climate, topography, and time, no simple scheme can cover the ground. Most of the world uses a system developed during the nineteenth century in the Soviet Union. In the United States and some other countries, however, a newer system is now in effect. The so-called Seventh Approximation, developed under a branch of the U.S. Department of Agriculture, has divided all soils into ten orders, with various subdivisions of each.

EROSION AND MASS WASTING

Erosion is the transportation of material under the influence of a medium, usually water but sometimes wind or ice. The movement of loose material without a medium, such as a loosened rock rolling downhill, is usually regarded as *mass wasting* rather than erosion in a strict sense. Both of these processes most often depend upon slope and tend to move material downhill

Soil horizons

O: Nonmineral, organic debris

A: Clay, silt, sand, and organic
matter. Commonly dark

—— *Transition*

B: Clay, silt, sand with little organic
matter. Richer in clay, iron, and
alumina from above. Commonly
lighter than A

—— *Transition*

C: Fragments of parent material,
possibly with some material
leached from above.

—— *Transition*

D: Parent material (bedrock or sediment)

(a)   (b)

Figure 4-7 Soil profile. (a) Idealized soil profile in a relatively humid temperate climate. (b) Photo of an actual profile; the c horizon begins at about 3 feet. *(Courtesy of U.S.D.A. Soil Conservation Service.)*

to lower elevations. For the Himalayas or the plains of Kansas, the effective bottom of the hill is sea level, and in this sense the sea is the *base level* of continental erosion. Actually, major rivers can erode their channels below sea level, probably more than 100 meters as in the case of the Amazon.

Mass Wasting Downslope movement, solely under the influence of gravity, occurs to dry or water-lubricated material that loses cohesion. The movement may be imperceptible, as in *soil creep*. Soil or regolith may move slowly downhill when excessive rain or freezing and thawing occurs; even wandering herds of cattle can cause the soil to be slightly unstable on some slopes. The movement is recognized often only by slanted telephone poles or fences (Figure 4-8). On the other hand, mass wasting may be very perceptible. Rockslides, or avalanches when snow and ice enter the process, have done enormous damage upon occasion. Earthquakes occasionally are the cause of the loss of cohesion of large masses of material, and one off the coast of Peru in 1970 triggered an avalanche in the Andes Mountains. An enormous quantity of rock debris, snow, and ice slid down the slopes of Mount Huascaran and down the inhabited valley below. The vertical drop totaled about 3500 meters and, at speeds of some 400 kilometers per hour (250 miles per hour), some 20,000 to 30,000 people were buried in less than 4 minutes.

EROSIONAL PROCESSES   Most erosion is by running water; wind and glaciers are secondary. When snow melts or rain falls, some water enters the ground; this groundwater will be discussed later. If enough water falls with sufficient rapidity, the ground will become saturated and the excess will flow downslope over the surface. This *runoff* is divisible into two categories, *sheet flow* and *channel flow*. In combination they are the prime movers of surface materials. They and all other erosive and mass wasting processes ultimately transport crustal material to the sea, the world's base level.

The worldwide rate at which these processes have been lowering the surface of the land is estimated to be about 2.5 centimeters per 1000 years. The land elevation now averages about 850 meters above the sea, and so in a few tens of million of years will *all* the land be gone, transported, ion by ion and grain by grain, to the sea? There is no evidence this has ever happened during geologic history, but the configurations of the continents and the amounts exposed as land have indeed varied widely through time. Probably climatic and topographic variations even have allowed much higher erosional rates, but isostasy, volcanism, and mountain building have always provided new land. Human beings have unquestionably altered the future in this regard, for deforestation and agricultural practices have exposed vast areas to increased erosion. Some workers have calculated the present worldwide rate of erosion to be more than *double* that before the use of axe and plow.

Sheet flow is the downslope movement of water in the form of thin sheets, or films, of fluid which flow in no particular path such as a stream does. The flow often creates rills and transient grooves in the surface, but by

Figure 4-8   Soil creep.

and large it is an inconspicuous but remarkably effective process of erosion (Figure 4-9). One of the most effective aids to sheet-flow erosion is the impact of raindrops. The energy of impact loosens and scatters soil particles and facilitates their transport downhill by the unchanneled runoff. Both the effect of raindrops and the velocity and transport capacity of sheet flow are increased where vegetation is sparse. This is how the agricultural errors of soil nutrient depletion (overfarming, overgrazing, and noncontour plowing) have allowed good soil to wash away. In the late 1960s a national inventory indicated erosion was the dominant conservation problem on about one-half of the agricultural land of the United States. Although most farmers in the United States have been practicing soil conservation for many years, in much of the world destructive farming practices are still prevalent. Most land in the world has some slope; even though farming tends to be practiced on fairly level land, only one-third of the crop land in the United States is sufficiently flat to have minimal erosion problems. Although quantitative data for the world are lacking, there is little doubt that sheet flow is the *major* erosive process on land.

Channel flow is the downslope movement of water in more-or-less permanent channels, that is streams. In a given drainage region very little of the area is occupied by channels, and although streams do erode within these channels, they are mainly *transporters* of material. The material being transported by streams is mostly brought to them by relatively unchanneled water, sheet flow, flowing down the surrounding slopes.

Figure 4-9 The effects of sheet flow on a barren slope. *(Courtesy of U.S.D.A., Soil Conservation Service.)*

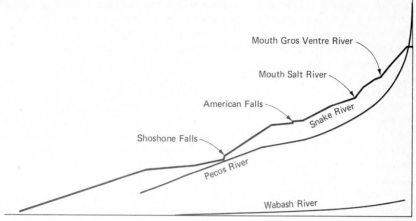

(Vertical scale exaggerated over 250 times)

Figure 4-10 Profiles of three rivers of the United States. The Wabash River has come closest to producing the smooth concave curve that characterizes maturity and equilibrium. The Snake River, which descends over 2300 meters in its 1500-kilometer-length, has a lot of erosion and deposition yet to undergo before all its irregularities are smoothed. *(After H. Gannett, United States Geological Survey.)*

Once within the stream the material in transport is the *stream load*. This material is carried in three ways: as the *dissolved load*, the *suspended load*, and the *bed load*. Before examining the load, it is necessary to gain some insight into the stream.

The total load a stream is capable of moving depends upon the amount of water it is carrying and the velocity with which that water flows. The most practical parameter of quantity is *discharge* (Q), the amount of water passing a plane across the stream during a given time. This is a product of velocity and the cross-sectional area of the stream: Q = width × depth × velocity. If discharge increases after a rain, the channel of the stream will change too. As the relation between Q and the stream parameters is maintained, velocity will increase and subsequent bed erosion will cause a depth and perhaps a width increase. The water and channel are in close relation and one cannot be altered without affecting the other.

The velocity of stream flow is dependent not only on channel configuration and quantity of water but on slope as well. This slope, or *gradient*, of a river generally decreases downstream, as shown by a plot of the downstream profile (Figure 4-10). Since stream velocity increases with increased slope, it was long thought that rivers flowed less swiftly as they progressed toward base level, but a tumbling mountain stream may actually have a lower velocity than what appears to be a gently flowing large river. Several factors contribute to this. Frictional losses in a stream cause a lower velocity. In general, more water in contact with the channel perimeter and with the atmosphere tends to lower flow speed. A very narrow, deep stream or a wide, very shallow stream has a higher proportion of bed and atmosphere boundaries than one which is about as wide as it is deep. Therefore, a stream in a channel of the latter configuration, somewhat like a half-circle, will flow faster. A rough channel also increases the frictional losses, and so a boulder-strewn stream flows more slowly than one with a smooth bed, other things being equal.

Each water molecule in a stream does not flow directly in the direction the stream flows. In nature, nearly all surficial flow is *turbulent*; the water is moving up, down, even opposite to the overall average movement downstream (Figure 4-11). The most turbulence is near the stream-bed interface, and this is where the lowest velocities are found. In general, the highest velocity in a relatively straight stream is in mid-channel at about 0.2 to 0.3 of the depth below surface. The average velocity, used for computing discharge, is often taken as that at 0.6 of the depth (Figure 4-12).

The mountain stream is usually relatively shallow, and so little of its water is remote enough from the bed with all its turbulence-causing effects to allow the overall flow to be as rapid as that of a deeper, larger stream. As tributaries contribute additional water further downstream, the discharge increases, the depth and width increase and allow less turbulence and frictional losses, and

Figure 4-11 (a) *Laminar flow.* Water moving at a fraction of a centimeter per second may have molecular movement along smooth lines, even when encountering a particle. This type of flow is not typical in natural streams, but is typical of groundwater flow. (b) *Turbulent flow.* The molecular paths of water form complex eddies moving in all directions. The particles of the suspended load follow similar paths. This multidirectional flow is superimposed on the average direction, which is downstream. Turbulent flow is typical in streams.

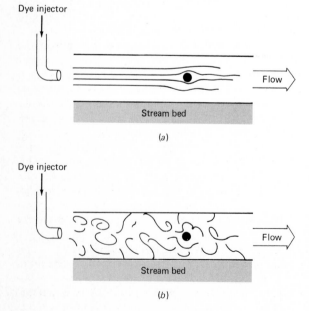

Dye injector

Flow

Stream bed

(a)

Dye injector

Flow

Stream bed

(b)

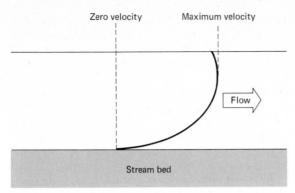

Figure 4-12   Velocity profile of a typical stream. The maximum rate of flow is approximately 0.2 of the depth, the average is flow 0.6 of the depth, and at the bed the flow is essentially 0.

so the velocity tends to increase. Commonly, small streams with relatively steep gradients may have an average velocity of less than 2 meters per second at flood stage, while a major river with a much lower gradient may have a flow closer to 3 meters per second at flood stage.

STREAM LOAD   The *dissolved load*, ions of various types carried in solution, does not affect stream flow. It does, of course, contribute to the removal of material from land and ultimately to the addition of material to the sea. The average amount of dissolved material in fresh waters is probably around 200 parts per million but, of course, there is wide variability. This visually unnoticeable portion of stream load is commonly about 30 percent of the total load of major streams such as the Amazon or Mississippi.

The *bed load* usually consists principally of coarser particles from boulders down to sand. This material slides, rolls, bounces and, upon collision, may move in intermittent jumps. The movement is nearly always in the flow direction and is initiated by the impact of water on the particle. Since the flow rate in a stream is lowest at the bottom, larger particles, which project upward into the more rapid flow, will begin to move at lesser velocities than smaller ones. Pebbles usually begin to move before sand, and sand may move over a silty bed that is still stable. The largest particle a stream can transport determines that stream's *competence*. Velocity is the prime factor governing competence and, in general, a doubling of velocity results in an impact force quadruple that at the prior velocity. Realizing this unequal increase of force to velocity, it is not surprising that much of the coarsest material in a stream bed may undergo transport only during flood conditions.

The *suspended load* consists of fine particulate material that is held in suspension by turbulent water motion. Very fine sand, silt, and clay compose most of the suspended load of streams. These particles would fall to the stream bed if the water's path of movement were only in the flow direction.

The upward currents in the turbulent eddies common to all streams overcome gravitational forces and permit suspension. Of course, with changes in velocity and turbulence, some particles alternate between the bed and suspended fractions. In the case of a clear, swift stream there is simply an absence of finer material.

Probably 90 percent or more of the solids carried to the sea by streams is borne in suspension. The settling velocity of a particle must be equaled or exceeded by the effect of upward turbulence in the stream for the particle to remain in suspension. The finest sand has a terminal fall velocity through water of about 0.35 centimeters per second, whereas very fine silt will fall at about 0.0014 centimeters per second. In a nonturbulent situation fine sand falls 1 meter in less than 5 minutes; fine silt requires nearly 20 hours. Turbulent water, of course, keeps grains suspended for longer times, as the grains are moving upward part of the time. Therefore, the stronger the turbulent currents, the coarser the particle that may be maintained in suspension above the stream bed. Upon entering the sea, where turbulence is much less, coarser particles cannot be supported and fall out near shore. Fine silts and clays may be carried farther out to sea before settling to the bottom. Hence, the energy of moving water is the factor that separates solid particles into depositional size groups which lead to the formation of beds of sandstone, siltstone, and shale or mudstone.

THE DEPOSITS OF STREAMS   Variations in topography, rock type, soil, and climate along a stream's path, plus the effect of the earth's rotation, have prevented the creation of the euphonious saying "straight as a stream." Streams wander, and once a curve begins it tends to become accentuated. Figure 4-13 shows that the highest stream velocity shifts from midstream to the outside of a curve. Bank erosion is increased along this higher-velocity zone, the curve becomes tighter, and when it becomes looplike it is a *meander*. Rivers may erode downward, but more regularly they erode laterally. As they do so, they leave channel deposits behind.

The area over which a stream has migrated during its history normally determines the breadth of the stream valley. The width of this valley also normally determines the sideward extent of floodwaters when the stream overflows its banks. Since flooding is more evident and rapid than lateral migration, the relatively broad plain bordering major streams is called the *floodplain* (Figure 4-14). Two types of sediments are characteristic of floodplains: those channel deposits the river left during lateral migration and those that settled out of suspension during overbank floods.

Floodplains, being flat and fertile, are often inhabited by humans. The floodplains of the Nile, Tigris, and Euphrates Rivers were the site of the earliest civilizations. Periodic flooding provides new soil material, and floodplains have been farmed for thousands of years without the extensive need for fertilizers. Dams built to limit the destructive nature of floods limit their constructive nature too.

When a stream reaches a local base level and loses competence, much of its load may be deposited. If the base level is a body of water a *delta* may form, and if its base level is an abrupt lessening of gradient on land an *alluvial fan* may form (Figure 4-15).

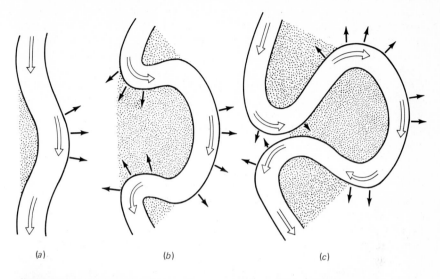

(a)   (b)   (c)

(d)

Figure 4-13 Meander formation. In a straight channel the maximum flow rate (broad arrows) is normally in midstream. When a curve begins, the maximum flow shifts to the outside of that curve and causes an increase in the rate of bank erosion. Erosion progresses (small arrows) and the two curves inside the bend converge. The curve is accentuated into a meander, and when the two curves meet and cut the bend off, an oxbow lake may form. [(d) Courtesy of P. A. Rahm.]

Figure 4-14 Two small foodplains meeting near the Uinta Mountains of Utah. Note the two flat terraces to the left. These are portions of previous floodplains; the streams have since cut downward to their present levels, probably in response to continued elevation of the area.

Figure 4-15 Alluvial fans are produced by small streams as the streams lose competence upon emerging from the mountain.

EROSIONAL RATES   Of all the material being eroded on land, only a small part is carried directly to the sea. Most remains, temporarily at least, as deposits on the land. We have referred to the fact that the deforestation and farming of land have increased erosional rates. The world's largest single transporter of eroded material is the Amazon. Draining an area nearly equal to that of the conterminous United States, it has a discharge over 10 times that of the Mississippi. The climate, topography, and vegetation cover in its drainage basin is significantly different from that of the United States, but the area is largely unaffected by humans. Its suspended load alone is about 500 million tons per year.

Given the differences in their discharges, one might expect the Mississippi to carry a suspended load equal to about 10 percent that of the Amazon, or 50 million tons per year; instead it carried an average of 344 million tons per year between 1949 and 1966! Prior to 1952 it was not uncommon for the Mississippi River to carry a yearly suspended load in excess of the Amazon's! Soil conservation practices were responsible for the reduced rate. It is estimated that prior to modern times, 9.3 billion tons of material were moved by rivers to the seas each year. Now it is estimated that 25 billion tons are removed annually! The effects of this increased rate of a natural process are speculative, but surely such a removal rate of soil and nutrients bodes ill for the world's agricultural future.

GROUNDWATER

Most of the liquid nonmarine water of the world is *in* the ground, not *on* it as lakes and streams. Yet this rain-provided water is not the only type found in the subsurface environment. Saline water is commonly encountered at depth during drilling through sedimentary strata for oil, or occasionally in an attempt to find fresh water. This *connate water* was entrapped in spaces among grains of sediment deposited in the shallow seas which commonly covered major portions of continents in the past. This type of groundwater may act to force associated petroleum to a well, but it is generally not available for use by plants or animals.

The water that seeps downward into regolith or soil after a rain is known as *meteoric water*. It is this groundwater that is used by rooted plants, that fulfills many of the requirements of humans, and that supplies streams so that they flow between rains. This water may move laterally through the ground, for example, down-valley toward streams and lakes or toward wells as water is removed. The flow is normally slow and nonturbulent.

During a rain the soil may become saturated with water; all the pore spaces are filled. After the rain ceases, some water will continue to percolate downward until the soil can hold no more. Two relatively distinct zones are formed. The upper, *unsaturated zone* has water on the surfaces of the soil particles and air in the pores. The lower, *saturated zone* has its pore spaces completely filled with water. The boundary between the zones defines the *water table* (Figure 4-16). The pore water in the lower zone is capable of direct flow, while water in the unsaturated zone is held to the particles by surface tension forces and will not freely flow. When a well penetrates the saturated zone, the water entering the well normally stabilizes at a level

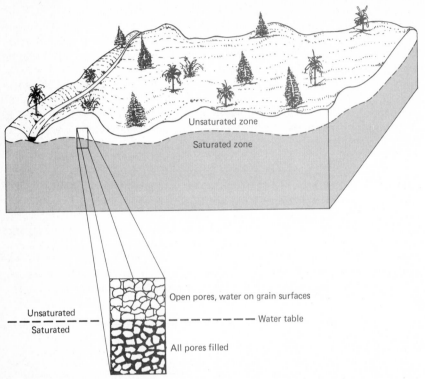

Unsaturated zone

Saturated zone

Open pores, water on grain surfaces

Unsaturated

Saturated

Water table

All pores filled

Figure 4-16 The water table is the boundary between the unsaturated zone and the saturated zone. It is easily measured since it is the depth at which water stands in a well. This diagram is typical of a relatively humid region where the water table is close to the surface and intersects the stream.

defining the water table. The rootlets of plants are capable of extracting the water from the unsaturated zone, but since water there will not flow, humans must seek their supply below the water table, in the saturated zone.

The level of the water table is variable according to topography and climate. Usually only a few meters below the surface in relatively humid areas, it may be very deep in deserts. In a subdued way, the water table conforms to the shape of the land surface, but normally it is nearer the surface in a valley than on a hill.

The movement of water through a porous soil or rock depends upon the nature of the pore spaces. The amount of pore space, *porosity*, is expressed as the percentage of a given total volume of material that consists of voids. Loose sand may have 30 percent porosity; sandstone, in which some space is occupied by a cementing or grain-binding mineral, commonly has 5 to 20 percent porosity.

A distinct body of gravel, sand, sandstone, or other porous medium through which groundwater moves is known as an *aquifer* (Figure 4-17). However, the presence of porosity does not guarantee that water will flow through the pores. The capacity of a sediment or rock to *transmit* a fluid is a measure of its *permeability*. If the pores are not joined together, for example, if a sandstone has all its grains tightly cemented together, water cannot flow through it. Or, if the pore spaces are too small, usually the case in very fine-grained materials such as clays and silts, too little of the water is free from the molecular forces binding it to the grain surfaces to permit flow. Shales may have 20 percent porosity but are nearly impermeable. Household septic systems in nonurban areas must be placed in soil with sufficient ability to disperse waste water. Many areas are regulated and require a test of the soil's ability to allow percolation of water before building permits are issued. A clay-rich soil may flunk a "perk" test because of its low permeability.

It is a misconception to imagine that underground water flows in hidden streams, or that a "pool" of oil is something like an underground lake. True, there are occasional underground streams, but they are simply using the path provided by a cavern that resulted from chemical solution, usually of limestone. In some areas where limestone is the predominant bedrock, cavern formation may be very extensive. Most caverns are thought to have formed below the water table by the dissolving action of groundwater. When the water table drops or the land rises, the caverns are modified by subsurface streams. In some humid areas the topography may be so strongly

Figure 4-17 Artesian flow. The aquifer is a permeable bed, here overlain by an impermeable confining bed. The confining bed causes a pressure head to exist as it permits water to stand at a high level near the intake area. When a well taps the aquifer, the pressure will force the water to rise above the aquifer, sometimes flowing freely at the surface. An artesian well may be many kilometers away from the intake area.

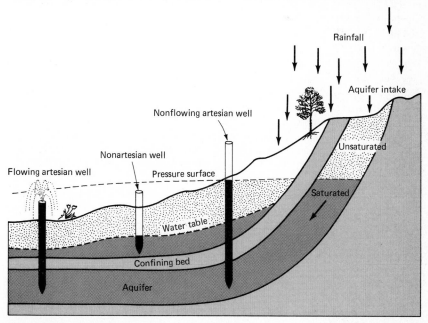

Figure 4-18 Karst topography in Puerto Rico *(Courtesy of A. Curet.)*

governed by cavern-forming processes that the name *karst* is given to this terrain (Figure 4-18). Cavern formation becomes extensive and the area is dotted with sinkholes as cave ceilings collapse at the surface. Small surface streams may be rare, having disappeared down sinkholes. The limestone surface becomes relatively dry as water is not retained near the surface, and small limestone hills form from the continual chemical weathering. The peculiar forms of these hills have given rise to many local names for them, from *haystack* to, in Puerto Rico, *pepino*, Spanish for "cucumber."

WIND

Wind, as an agent of erosion, is a minor factor in vegetated areas, but is a common material transporter in coastal and desert regions.

Deserts cover about one-eighth of the world's land surface, and lack of continuous plant cover permits the wind full access to the ground surface. The wind load is all solid particulate material and, like streams, has a bed load and a suspended load. When wind velocities are high enough, some sand begins to roll. Upon impact with other grains the sand will bounce and enter the airstream. Upon descent on other grains, the transfer of momentum causes them to bounce and roll also. If the wind maintains its velocity, the floor of a sandy desert becomes a moving mass of grains. Usually the sand bounces only a few centimeters off the desert floor, but if some larger pieces of rock, pebbles for instance, are hit, the falling grain bounces higher. Sand rarely rises to 2 meters. Large portions of many deserts are floored with rock fragments, so-called stony deserts. The wind has removed sand from the surface faster than it can be supplied. These fragments are known as *ventifacts* if they show the effects of sandblasting and are polished and faceted.

The sand often accumulates into mounds and ridges called *dunes*, not only in the sandy parts of a desert but also scattered about on stony desert.

These dunes are transient bodies, and as sand is carried up the windward side, is borne over the crest, and rolls down the steeper lee, the dune "moves." Some dunes grow to heights of over 100 meters and commonly migrate several meters a year. Depending upon the sand supply, presence or absence of desert vegetation, strength and constancy of wind direction, the dunes assume various forms. Windblown sand deposits are well known and commonly exhibit large-scale cross-bedding, generally produced on the lee face (Figure 4-19).

Particulate matter may be carried upward into the air and supported by turbulent eddies during its transport. This material constitutes the suspended load. A "sandstorm" is really a silt storm above the first meter or so, since air cannot maintain sand in suspension with the efficiency of turbulent water. Wind, usually not having the relative permanence of a stream, tends to deposit its suspended load fairly soon and near its origin. Some storms, however, have carried silt thousands of meters into the air and for thousands of kilometers laterally. Normally the wind-borne particles fall and make up a minor fraction of the already present soil or regolith.

However, over some large areas downwind from major deserts or in areas where receding continental glaciers have left large amounts of silt-sized rock flour for wind to transport, the deposits are thick. Wind deposits from either of these origins are known as *loess*. Loess generally forms unstratified deposits, blanketing both hills and valleys of the former surface. The silt-sized particles are predominantly quartz with feldspars, mica, and other minerals making up various fractions of the material. There is usually very little clay. (You should be able to propose a reason for that based upon your knowledge of how and where clay most commonly forms.) The angularity of many of the grains and the relative constancy of size give a cohesiveness to loess uncommon to other loose sediment. Where exposed in a stream bank or road cut, it will maintain a very steep or even vertical face (Figure 4-20).

GLACIERS

Only about 2.8 percent of the water on this planet is nonmarine, and of this small portion, nearly 80 percent is frozen. It can be argued that we still live in a glacial age, but most of that ice is so remote from population centers that we tend to ignore it. On Antarctica, where about 90 percent of the world's ice and hence most of the world's fresh water is located, and on Greenland, where another 8 percent is located, the ice in places is over 4000 meters thick. Mute testimony of a changing earth is given by the fact that one can study the effects of glaciers near Chicago or Berlin since these areas became ice-free only a few thousand years ago.

The Origin of Glaciers   When, over a long period of years, more snow falls in winter than melts in summer, glacier ice will form. Within a snowfield the conversion to ice may begin first by surficial thawing and refreezing. Later, the weight of newer snow compacts the older snow, and processes such as evaporation and condensation add ice to forming grains. The once nearly

(a)

(b)

Figure 4-19   (a) A modern sand dune. The principal wind direction is from the left; sand is transported up the low slope and rolls down the steeper leeside. (b) Cross-bedding characteristic of dune deposition in a sandstone of Jurassic age over 130 million years old.

Figure 4-20   Loess. This deposit is of silt-sized material transported to the site by wind. Note how loess maintains a nearly vertical slope. *(Courtesy of Mr. W. Burns, Iowa State Highway Department.)*

ephemeral flakes disappear and the hard and granular corn snow familiar to spring skiers forms. At about 30 meters deep, when further compaction forces out air and the granules intergrow, the white ice becomes dense and bluish *glacier ice.* This type of ice may form at high elevations in any latitude (there are glaciers near the equator) or at low elevations in colder climates. At a depth not far below that at which glacier ice forms, the pressure from above causes the ice to lose its brittle nature and act as a highly viscous liquid. To be a glacier, the ice must flow. The two most commonly studied types of glaciers are those in mountains which normally flow down preexisting valleys (Figure 4-21) and those which form ice sheets over continents and, when advancing, can cover almost any terrain if thick enough.

Glacial Flow and Erosion   Depending upon environmental conditions, both within and external to the glacier, two general types of ice movement may occur. One is *slippage* of the glacier over its bed, and the other is *plastic flow* within the ice itself. It is relatively easy to measure ice movement at the surface of a glacier; daily surveys of stakes placed in the ice will indicate the flow rate. Flow rates are commonly less than a meter per day although much higher rates are known. It is difficult to determine which type of flow, if both are occurring, is responsible for what portion of the total movement of the glacier. Some glaciers are frozen to their bed and no slippage occurs. To get to the bed and determine this would seem to require only periodic measurements of a borehole to bedrock. If it is realized that plastic flow well above the

Figure 4-21 A valley glacier in Canada. Note the plasticity of the ice as it spreads leaving the valley. *(Courtesy of J. Neimi.)*

bottom will rapidly close the borehole, it is easy to see why glacial flow mechanics is a subject not fully understood.

In general, glaciers are divisible into two zones, one of *accumulation* and one of *wastage* (Figure 4-22). In the zone of accumulation more snow falls than is removed by such processes as melting and evaporation. In the zone of wastage, farther down-glacier, depletion of ice exceeds accumulation. The processes of depletion most often involve melting, evaporation, and sublimation (ice entering the vapor state without passing through a liquid state). Since all may operate, to avoid cumbersome explanations of which depletion mechanisms are occurring, the loss of glacial ice by whatever natural means is known as *ablation*. If accumulation exceeds ablation, a glacier will advance. If the reverse is true, the glacier will recede at its terminus. Note, however, that even if the terminus of a glacier is receding, the ice *within* the glacier may still be moving forward.

As a glacier moves over its bed, large pieces of loosened rock from the bed may become incorporated into the ice. Freeze-thaw action, perhaps of summer meltwaters seeping beneath the ice, may raise rock fragments above the surrounding bed so that the ice can remove them. The fragments plucked from the bed not only alter the shape of the valley or terrain over which the glacier moves, but also act as tools to abrade, gouge, and scratch the bedrock. Rock above the surface of valley glaciers is often loosened by frost action and falls onto the ice. The glacier thus obtains a load of rock debris, and some glaciers are so loaded that the ice appears more black than blue.

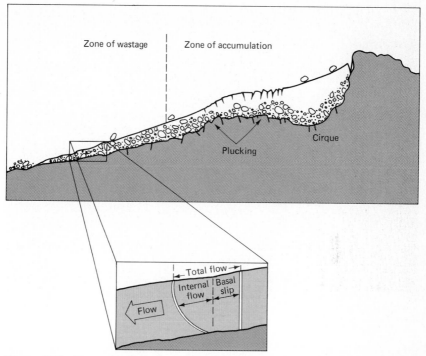

Figure 4-22 The main diagram shows an idealized profile of a valley glacier. The extended view of a small area (not showing the load of rock debris), illustrates two types of ice flow. On the right a borehole through the ice to the rock bed is shown. To the left is the *same* borehole later in time. Plastic flow within the ice has deformed the hole in the flow direction. At the glacier's base, slippage has also occurred and contributed to the overall flow. Some glaciers are frozen to their base and no slippage occurs.

While climatic changes may cause a glacier to disappear, its load is left behind and its erosional effects may be very evident on the landscape.

Glaciated Terrain The sculpturing of bedrock, mostly by plucking and abrasion, often leaves very clear evidence of glaciation. A U-shaped valley, in contrast to the V-shape of most stream valleys, is a distinct glacial feature (Figure 4-23). At the upper end, or beginning, of such a valley, a *cirque*, a bowl-shaped depression, is common. During a continental-scale glaciation, sea level is lowered significantly because so much water becomes ice. In the geologically recent past, sea level was at least 100 meters lower than now. Glacial valleys which were then formed along coasts have since been drowned by the rising sea and are known as *fiords*. Striations and grooves in bedrock are very common to glaciated areas and often indicate flow direction (Figure 4-24).

Figure 4-23   A U-shaped glacial valley in Yosemite Park, California.

Glacial deposits are known by the general term *drift*. The name is a carry-over from the days before the former presence of continental ice sheets was realized. It was thought that the erratic boulders resting on the land's surface far from any easily conceived source had drifted there, perhaps in a berg during the flood of Noah's time.

The streams from glacial meltwaters may carry glacial debris and sort

Figure 4-24   Pleistocene glacial striations on bedrock.

Figure 4-25 Till, an unsorted, unstratified deposit of particles ranging from clay to boulders in size.

and deposit it in stratified layers. These deposits of glacial outwash may vary little from any other stream deposit, but when recognized are termed *stratified drift*. The most easily recognized deposits of a glacier are unstratified drift let down by melting ice and are known as *till*. Till is unsorted material that commonly has a broad range of particle sizes; in fact, it is often referred to as *boulder clay* (Figure 4-25). Deposits of till may consist of ridges of material directly deposited from the ablating ice, known as *moraines*. *Terminal* and *recessional* moraines mark the positions of a glacier's free margin along the course of its retreat.

A glacier deposits these moraines when it is in temporary balance between accumulation and wasting and is not advancing. During one of these stillstands the ice still moves forward *within* the glacier, carrying debris to the ablating front (Figure 4-26). While the axis of such a moraine is normal to the flow direction, other types of moraines may form parallel to the flow. If the glacier retreated at a fairly constant rate, the till may have been deposited more uniformly. In this case a blanket of till known as *ground moraine* results. Morainal deposits are extremely common in those areas of North America covered during the last continental glaciation, which only ended (?) some 6000 years ago in central Canada (Figure 4-27).

Among the most pleasing legacies of the last ice sheet are the many lakes it created. Erosional depressions in bedrock, moraine-dammed drainage, and depressions in the drift from the melting of buried broken-off blocks of ice, all have allowed Ontario, Canada, its license plate motto "100,000

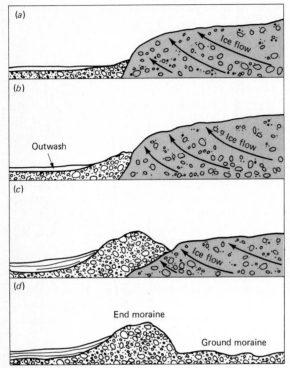

Figure 4-26 End moraine. As the glacier more or less stabilizes at its terminus, the ice within is still moving and carrying debris to the ablating surface. A ridge of till forms. Some material will be carried away by the meltwater and form outwash deposits. When the glacier becomes more unstable and wastage exceeds accumulation over a long period, it will recede at a more constant rate and deposit till as ground moraine. *(From R. F. Flint et al. Glacial Map of North America.)*

lakes.'' If for nothing else, we owe an aesthetic debt to glaciers for producing some of the beautiful scenery in mountain ranges all over the world. Just one leisurely boat trip up a Norwegian fiord almost justifies the frustrations of trying to dig up a garden in boulder clay. The historical aspects of the latest major glaciation are covered in Chapter 8.

THE LANDSCAPE
The shape of the exposed surface of the earth's continents is created predominently by running water. As the forces at interacting plate boundaries and vertical isostatic movements cause the elevation of a crustal mass, destruction of that mass begins. Disintegration, decomposition, and erosion will eventually remove the Himalayas. The realization of the temporal nature of all earthly things is a relatively recent entrant into the minds of Western people. Usually the elevated surfaces are lowered so slowly, in human time

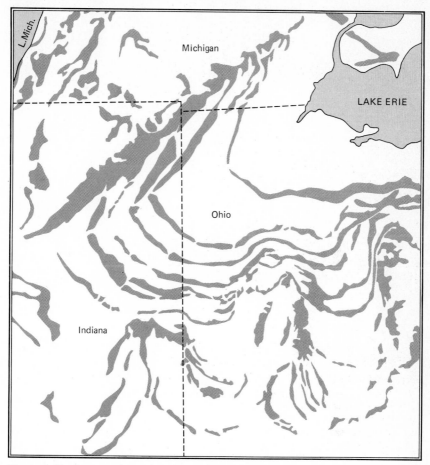

Figure 4-27 Some end moraines in the Great Lakes area.

frames, that it goes unnoticed. The landscapes we see now, in all their variety, are interim stages in a battle between upbuilding and down-wearing processes. Although variable in rate according to rock type, climate, and elevation, theoretically the almost ceaseless down-wearing processes will triumph.

Based on this idea, a concept of the progressional development of landforms was proposed at about the beginning of this century. Figure 4-28 illustrates the three stages of *youth, maturity*, and *old age* in this series. The final result, as down-wearing processes overcome the forces that caused and, in part, isostatically maintained the crustal elevation, is a *peneplain*. A peneplain, or "almost a plain," is a nearly featureless surface, usually once at or near sea level, that was created by *erosion*. Most geologists accept some regional surfaces as peneplains. Extensive peneplains are not the rule

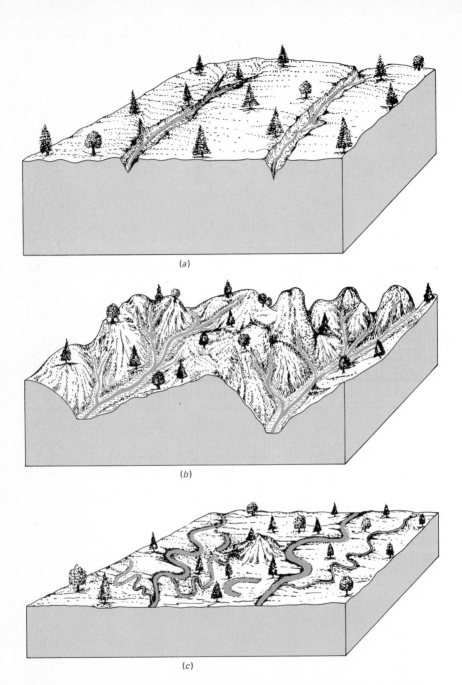

Figure 4-28 Stages in an idealized erosion sequence. (*a*) A youthful topography. Most of the land is in uplands between streams which are narrow, fairly straight, and eroding downward to form narrow V-shaped valleys. (*b*) A mature topography. Most of the land is in slope and the terrain is most rugged. The streams have eroded laterally and floodplains begin form. (*c*) An old-age topography. Most of the land has been eroded so that strong slopes are absent, base level is close, the streams have extensive meanders, and the entire surface approaches the condition of a peneplain.

Figure 4-29   A youthful stream in a mature topography.

on land long exposed to erosion because the planet is geologically too active to commonly permit their development. Sequences in landform development are a trend through time, but the interpretation of the history of any broad landform is octopusian in its complexity (Figure 4-29). Only specific knowledge of all the processes involved allows a reasonably complete understanding.

FIVE

TIME, FOSSILS, AND THE ROCK RECORD

If one desires to understand the present state of humans and their institutions, one must have some knowledge of their history. To determine where we are going, it is wise to know where we have been. To understand very much about the earth or even a single rock it is even more obvious that some knowledge of the past is requisite. Since nature has provided no historical writings, the earth scientist must read some other records and try to place past events into some time frame. Our most familiar time frame is based on the year, with the zero point being the birth of Christ. Other civilizations and religions use or have used a basic unit close to a solar year, since recurring astronomic and seasonal events have made it our common reference. The zero point, however, varies and a Christian A.D. 2000 will be the Jewish 5761 and a Muslim 1378. Until this century geologists had no means of assigning events in earth history to any definitive yearly scheme and were forced to regard them in terms of *relative* time.

RELATIVE TIME
The basic units of relative time are *older* and *younger*. Without having even a reasonably firm idea of the age in years of the earth or the crustal rocks and fossils they studied, earlier geologists devised the geologic time scale (Figure 5-1). With much work and through many changes this time scale, in which a rock could be assigned to a particular position in time, came into general

RELATIVE LENGTH OF EACH ERA	ERAS	PERIODS	EPOCHS	MILLIONS OF YEARS AGO
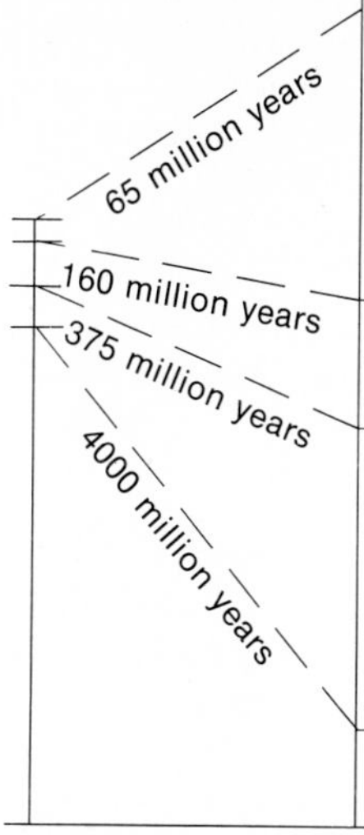 65 million years / 160 million years / 375 million years / 4000 million years	Cenozoic	Quaternary	Recent / Pleistocene	—2
		Tertiary	Pliocene / Miocene / Oligocene / Eocene / Paleocene	—25
	Mesozoic	Cretaceous / Jurassic / Triassic		65 / —135 / —190
	Paleozoic	Permian / Pennsylvanian / Mississippian / Devonian / Silurian / Ordovician / Cambrian		—225 / —230 / —325 / —350 / —400 / —430 / —500
	Precambrian			600

Age of Earth = 4600

Figure 5-1 Geologic time scale.

use. On the basis of a few general principles a particular rock unit might be assigned to, say, the Silurian period. This implied only that it was older than rocks of Devonian time and younger than those of Ordovician time. Such a scheme is fundamental if the complex history of an ever-changing earth is to be studied intelligently.

The time scale was developed largely in Britain and Western Europe in the eighteenth and nineteenth centuries. Many of the period names are derived from the areas where rocks of that age were first studied in detail. For example, the Ordovician period was first determined from studies of strata in Wales, and the Ordovices were an ancient Celtic tribe that inhabited the area. The old Roman name for Wales was Cambria, hence Cambrian. And rocks in the old Russian province of Perm near the Ural Mountains were used to define Permian. To assign strata in North America to these periods, it is necessary to establish evidence that these strata were deposited contemporaneously with those of the type section. Since the rocks themselves may have completely different lithologies, fossil evidence is the main criterion. Secondary type sections have been established on other continents to facilitate the task, but disputes to which period certain strata should be assigned are not unusual.

The era divisions are based on more fundamental changes in fossil populations, usually large-scale extinctions and appearances of new types. The suffix -zoic is from the Greek zoikos, meaning "pertaining to life"; paleozoic means "ancient life," mesozoic "middle life," and cenozoic "recent life."

PRINCIPLES OF RELATIVE TIME

Superposition   Superposition is a simple concept, but its application in the field is not always simple: *in an undisturbed sequence of layered sedimentary rock, each layer was formed after the one beneath it* (Figure 5-2).

Most rock exposed at the earth's surface is sedimentary, and most of these rocks were deposited in shallow seas which periodically covered portions of all continents. When these strata are relatively undisturbed, for instance in the Midwestern United States, their layering is still nearly horizontal, in the attitude of their deposition (Figure 5-3). It is easy to determine that an upper stratum is younger than one below. The relative time sequence is easily understood. But rocks of the same age may have been involved in, say, the Appalachian mountain-building event and became distorted or even turned up to a vertical position. The application of the idea of superposition now becomes more difficult.

Implicit in the idea of superposition is knowledge of which way was "up," for if a series of strata were completely overturned, the topmost would be older, not younger, than those below. In the strata distorted to vertical, perhaps a geologist could find raindrop impressions on some layer originally exposed to the Silurian atmosphere, a tidal flat perhaps. These are a clue to the original orientation, and which were the younger rocks could then be determined (Figure 5-4). We have crossed a mental boundary here, for without much thought we have assumed that what we see as raindrop

Figure 5-2 Superposition. The oldest rock is exposed on the surface between the rock towers and the youngest is on their tops. Since the strata are nearly horizontal and exposures are close, recognizing rocks of the same age from place to place is fairly easy. *(Monument Valley, Arizona; courtesy of Cristabel Grant.)*

(a)

(b)

Figure 5-3 Horizontality of strata. Most sediments are deposited in a layered fashion and, if undisturbed, the beds of rock they become are horizontal. (a) Some even-bedded Paleozoic strata of the central United States where stability has reigned for hundreds of millions of years. (b) Some Mesozoic strata near the Rocky Mountains. These too were originally horizontal but conditions were not stable, neither while deposition occurred (hence the different rock types) nor later when mountain-building forces tilted the beds.

(a)

(b)

Figure 5-4 *Problems in ancient "up"*. In (a), the strata directly in front of the geologists are nearly vertical. (After they had been turned up from horizontal and after an erosion surface developed, the lighter-colored sediments above, still horizontal, were deposited.) To determine whether the younger of the vertical strata is to the right or left (that is, which way was up) would require careful examination. Perhaps raindrop impressions similar to those in (b) would give the clue.

impressions on sediment today can be seen and used intelligently to determine which surface of a very ancient rock was exposed. Also we have assumed that the rock was deposited in an environment that is comparable to a modern one where rain could fall on an exposed surface of soft sediment. This is a logical assumption, and the governing concept is expressed as another principle relating to the past.

Uniformitarianism   *Any physical or biological feature of earth was produced by processes acting in accord with the laws of nature that now exist.*
   Without a philosophical acceptance of this principle of uniformitarianism the study of the earth's past becomes hopeless. Were the geologist to find a fossil of a marine organism in those same ancient strata, he or she would use both the raindrop impressions and the fossil to make additional logical assumptions about the environment of deposition and the character of past life. But this can be done only be rejecting an alternative: that the impressions and fossil came to be there by means beyond our understanding. Uniformitarianism is a rejection of supernatural causes (Figure 5-5).
   What is *not* implied by uniformitarianism is that things were always the same on earth or that processes always operated at the same rates as they now do. We may have no direct experience of studying erosional processes on a land comparable to that of a very early earth, with no rooted plants and with an oxygen-free atmosphere. But we can work with the rational assumption that, whatever occurred, the same laws governing physical and biological processes today governed those of the past.

Figure 5-5   Modern impressions of raindrops on soft sediment; compare with those shown in Figure 5-4 and produced over 225 million years ago.

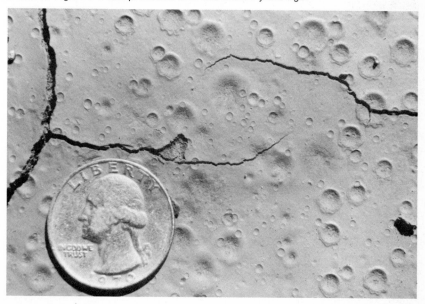

Faunal Succession   *Populations of organisms always change through time and once changed will not appear again in their previous form.*

Many sedimentary strata contain abundant fossils (Figure 5-6). If one studies the fossil populations from a thick sequence of strata, it is common to find that the physical nature of the individuals making up a population changes as one progresses upward or downward through the sequence. That is, the populations changed through time. As an example, suppose that in two beds of very similar shale, one a few meters above the other, several species of snail fossils were found. The snail types in one bed are all easily seen to differ from those in the other. The two shales do not seem to have been deposited in very different environments, so why are the fossils in them different? If the kind of snail fossils in the lower bed are nowhere found in strata above that bed, at least two explanations are possible. One is that some catastrophic event destroyed all the snails now seen as fossils in the lower bed and those in the upper bed are the product of a new creation of life. This is not only untenable under the idea of uniformitarianism but also, today, not very theologically acceptable. Two things lead to the rejection of the catastrophic idea: (1) fossils in different strata may differ only slightly and therefore seem to be related and (2) while some kinds of fossils in lower strata are never found in younger rocks, others associated with them are. How can only selected species be destroyed and their spatially close associates survive so their descendants can be fossilized later in time?

The alternative explanation is that the upper rocks contain snail fossils biologically related to the snails represented by the fossils in the lower stratum. The physical process of the deposition of muds, later to become shale, may not have changed through time, but organic change is constantly going on. This change, here manifested as changes in the shell morphology of the snails, is *evolution* (Figure 5-7). When the changes are of such a magnitude that a new species is considered to have evolved, the previous species, if never found in younger beds, is said to be extinct.

Some extinct species may have left direct descendants; others may not have. If the deposition of sediments has been relatively constant in an area, the fossils in different beds may differ in only small and subtle ways, for evolution can be a relatively gradual process. Often, however, the same types of fossils in adjacent beds may be easily differentiated. This is partly because most of geologic time has no physical representative in any one area in the form of sedimentary rock, and hence no vehicle exists for preservation of the life that existed. Also, evolution of new species can be relatively rapid and no population of forms transitional between different but directly related species ever existed. In a sequence of sedimentary strata the rocks themselves usually represent only a small part of the time involved from the deposition of the lowermost stratum to that of the topmost. (That is, most of geologic time is represented by bedding planes, the surfaces between rock layers; the planes represent periods of no deposition.) Probably less than 1 percent of the organisms that ever existed on earth are or will be known to us.

Faunal succession is what most easily enables geologists to place groups of rocks into fairly definite periods of relative geologic time. Rocks are usually placed into the time scale by being *correlated* with others whose age is known. This correlation often involves the physical nature and sequence of the strata, but since that may be repeated elsewhere in time, the nature of the fossils is the definitive criterion. If strata in Texas and strata in Montana contain populations of similar fossil assemblages, they may be regarded as approximate time equivalents. Without the use of fossil populations, which represent constant and nonrepetitive change, errors in correlation would be very common (Figure 5-8).

REAL TIME

If "real" time is considered to be that which can be expressed in years, until this century no means to assign definite ages to ancient rocks existed. A few centuries ago many considered the earth to be only a few thousand years old. During the nineteenth century this idea came into conflict with concepts derived from the study of depositional and erosional rates and with those derived from attempts to understand the history of organic evolution. Both required large amounts of time if uniformitarianism was to be accepted. For example, it was difficult to understand how the Alps came to be mountains in a few thousand years considering that many of the now-elevated rocks were deposited in seas. The lack of the fundamental understanding of faunal changes through time, coupled with a lack of appreciation for the great expanse of geologic time, even led to expectations of encountering dino-

Figure 5-6 Paleozoic corals in limestone.

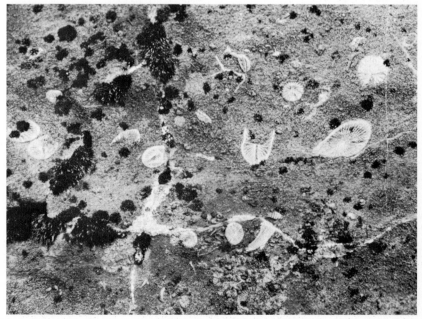

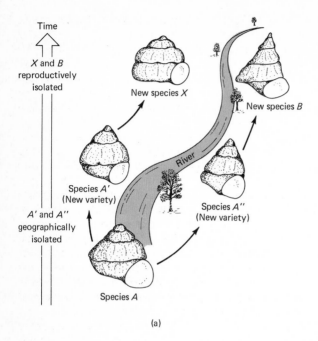

(a)

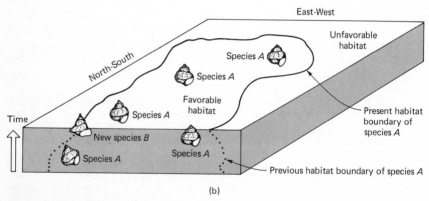

(b)

Figure 5-7 Evolution of new species. (a) One concept of speciation. A population of organisms (here snail species A) has become divided by a river; geographic isolation has occurred to some members of the population. Changes in the biologic nature of a population of interbreeding organisms are inevitable through time. Over millions of years it is not surprising that the separated populations change along somewhat different paths and two new species arose. Once the two populations have changed enough to prevent cross-population interbreeding with the production of fertile young, the speciation is complete. The river or any other isolating factor is then unnecessary, for the two groups have become isolated reproductively. Note that even if no geographic split in the original population had occurred, species A would still have changed through time and a new species (X) would have arisen.

(b) Another mechanism leading to speciation. The population of species A is limited in its geographic extent, perhaps by temperature, water depth, food supply, etc. At or

saurs (extinct for at least 65 million years) in remote valleys in Africa or South America.

Several ingenious and logical estimates of the age of the earth or its oceans were made, but for various reasons were in error or, if close to what we now believe, were more akin to educated guesses. The final scientifically acceptable estimation of the earth's age, prior to the discovery of the phenomenon which is the basis for our present methods, was made near the end of the last century. The eminent English physicist William Thompson (Lord Kelvin) worked out the earth's age based on studies of its heat flow. Although the sun provides nearly all our life-supporting heat, the earth also gives off heat. The quantity, about 40 calories each year per square centimeter of surface, is minute enough to be easily detected only if one descends into a deep mine or lowers a thermometer down a deep well. The assumption in Lord Kelvin's day was that all this heat was the product of an earth still cooling off from a once-molten state. He reasoned that if one could measure and estimate the total quantity of heat lost each year, then it would be possible to calculate how many years ago the earth had been too hot for water to exist as a liquid. This would give the age in years of the earliest sedimentary rocks. Even less time would be available for life and, therefore, the oldest fossils. Kelvin and his associates calculated that the earth reached its present state of solidification some 20 to 40 million years ago.

This was not enough time. How, with uniformitarianism concepts, could the vast amounts of sediment eroded from older, once-high mountain ranges be explained? Either much more time or vastly increased erosional rates in the past were required. How could mountains consisting of uplifted strata containing fossils which indicated the youngest rocks involved in the mountain building were very young in the geologic relative time scale have risen so rapidly? Catastrophe? Kelvin's logical data began to force recantations of some correct geological and biological theories.

At about this time, in 1896, the French physicist Becquerel exposed a photographic plate wrapped in opaque paper to rays, not of normal light, but emitted by a uranium compound. He discovered the phenomenon of *radioactivity*, a word coined by Marie Curie shortly after. The Curies expanded the study of radioactive minerals and discovered that these minerals gave off heat as well as various other emanations. Here was something Kelvin could not have known. It was soon calculated that most of the earth's heat could be

---

near its geographic boundaries survival may be a tenuous thing. The pressures of survival selection are strong and small biologic changes in the population are rapidly selected for or against.

Probably the most common mechanism for the production of new species has been by way of a combination of the ideas shown in (*a*) and (*b*). Isolation of a subpopulation near the periphery of the geographic-habitat range of the major population would result in (1) the rapid evolution of new species and (2) no gradual series of intermediate types between the new and previous species. Therefore, many of the gaps we find in the fossil record are more the product of evolutionary biology than the result of sedimentary geologic processes.

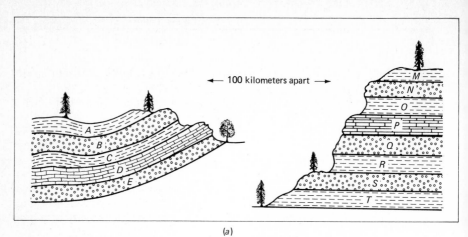

(a)

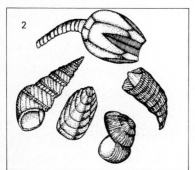

2

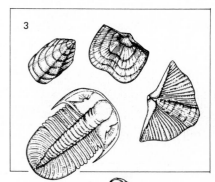

3

1

Found in both bed A and R

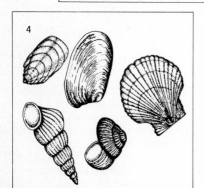

4

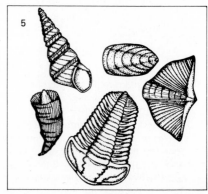

5

(b)

accounted for by the natural radioactive minerals in the earth's crustal rocks. Today only a small fraction of earth heat flow is considered to be residual heat from the formation of the planet. Time expanded with the expansion in knowledge.

RADIOMETRIC AGE DATING

In addition to heat, emissions from radioactive elements were found to be of three types:

1. *Gamma rays*, similar to the x-rays discovered before Becquerel's experiments, of very short wavelengths and of high penetration power

2. *Beta particles*, each consisting of an electron

3. *Alpha particles*, each consisting of two protons and two neutrons

In the case of the two particles, when an atom of an element spontaneously emits one of them, there is a change in the fundamental condition of the mother atom. In the case of an alpha particle the original atom has lost four subatomic particles. If only neutrons were lost, the atom would remain the same element, but would have less weight. Since an element is what it is according to the number of protons in its nucleus, the loss of two of them by alpha emission transforms it into another element. For example, if an atom of uranium (uranium has 92 protons) were to emit an alpha particle, it would have 90 protons and would not *be* uranium any longer, but would be thorium (which has 90 protons). Nature has always been achieving the alchemist's dream of transmuting one element into another.

When a beta particle (an electron) is emitted, it would seem to be no more than a typical chemical event, for atoms commonly give up electrons. But this electron is not from the "cloud" surrounding the nucleus, but is derived from the nucleus itself. Since there are no electrons in an atomic nucleus, this electron is thought to be a product of the breakdown of a neutron. When the uncharged neutron loses a negative charge by beta emission, it then has a positive charge. It has become, then, a proton. When the proton number changes, the element changes, and so again, spontaneously, some elements are transformed to other elements. Such spontaneous changes, or decay, have been occurring to certain unstable radioactive isotopes (see Chapter 2) of elements since the beginning of the earth. The decay continues until a stable isotope results. For example, the unstable

Figure 5-8 Correlation. If beds *A-E* were correlated with the *M-T* series only on the basis of rock types and their sequence, the match-up would likely be *A-M*, *B-N*, and so on. If fossils are used, a new interpretation is obligatory. If the fossils of group 1 were found in both *A* and *R*, the correlation changes to *A-R*, *B-S*, and so on. All the beds above (younger) than *R* at the eastern outcrop are missing to the west, probably eroded, maybe never deposited. Using the numbered groups of fossils and assuming each bed contains a group, what is their numerical order of age descending through beds *B*, *C*, *D*, and *E*?

"parent" material uranium 238 decays to stable lead 206, its "daughter" product.

How does all this relate to time measurements? Each radioactive emission takes place almost instantly, but in any measurable quantity of a parent element there is a very large number of atoms. Continuously, some are decaying to daughter elements; this is easily detected by the use of a geiger counter or similar instrument for detecting emissions. It is not predictable *which* individual atom will decay at any particular time, but given the large total number of atoms in a sample, statistically the *percentage* that will change in a given amount of time is measurable.

This rate of decay has led to the creation of a time parameter known as a half-life. The *half-life* of a radioactive isotope of an element is the time required for one-half of an original quantity of atoms to decay (Figure 5-9). Some unstable isotopes have half-lives of less than 1 second, others of billions of years. These rates have been experimentally determined, and the spontaneous decay rates seem to be unaffected by normal crustal pressures

Figure 5-9 Half-life. In the upper diagram the candle, with a half-life of 2 hours, is decaying to heat, light, and gases. The rate of change is linear. In the lower diagram a radioactive isotope of element *A* is decaying to element *B*; the half-life, like that of the candle, is 2 hours. After two half-lives (4 hours) the candle is gone, but one-quarter of radioactive element *A* still remains. The rate of change is exponential. During each half-life, one-half of the quantity that was there at the start of that half-life will decay.

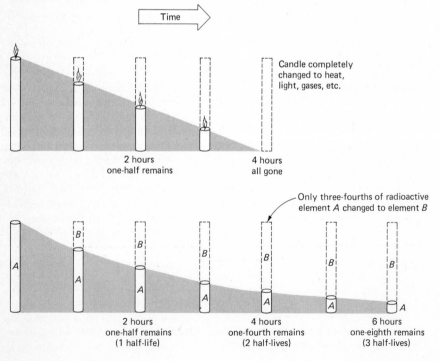

Time

Candle completely changed to heat, light, gases, etc.

2 hours
one-half remains

4 hours
all gone

Only three-fourths of radioactive element *A* changed to element *B*

2 hours
one-half remains
(1 half-life)

4 hours
one-fourth remains
(2 half-lives)

6 hours
one-eighth remains
(3 half-lives)

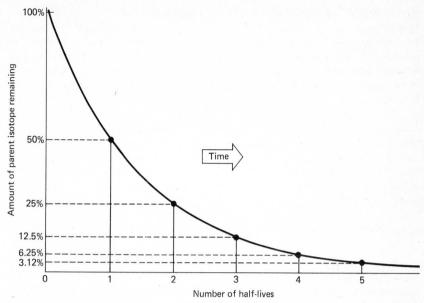

Figure 5-10 A graph of the number of half-lives passed compared with the amount of parent isotope remaining.

and temperatures. So they seem not to have varied significantly in the past.

Consider this simple theoretical example. In a sample of some igneous rock, common granite, for example, among the countless atoms of its component elements certain small quantities of a radioactive element A were detected. It is known that this particular unstable isotope A decays to a stable isotope of another element, B, and the half-life of A is known to be 100 years. If there were equal numbers of A and B in the sample, say 1000 atoms of each, then *originally*, when the rock crystallized and there was as yet no B, there were 2000 atoms of A. But, since one-half has decayed to B, one half-life has passed and the rock crystallized 100 years ago. One-half of the remaining quantity of A decays during each successive half-life, leaving 1000 atoms after 100 years, 500 after 200 years, 250 after 300 years, and 125 after 400 years, or four half-lives, have passed (Figure 5-10).

In actuality, radioactive decay systems may be quite complex, and the measurements of the quantities and types of isotopes involved require very sophisticated equipment. Nevertheless, the concept is relatively simple. One thing that must be considered is whether the parent-daughter isotopes are contained within a *closed system*. A closed system means that neither parent nor daughter isotopes have been added to or removed from the system by any process other than radioactive decay. Such a system might be a crystal of a particular mineral that has not been subject to chemical activity or excessive heat; in such a crystal, no parent or daughter isotopes should have escaped from or entered the crystal.

SYSTEMS OF RADIOMETRIC AGE DETERMINATION

The initial idea that certain rocks could be dated, not relatively but in terms of years by using radiometric methods, was put forth soon after the turn of the century. The practice is common today and, although various isotopic systems are used for specific problems, only a few are in widespread use. For most geologic problems the systems must involve isotopes with reasonably long half-lives.

Uranium to Lead   All isotopes of uranium (U), and there are about 15 known, are radioactive. Two are relatively common, in very small amounts, in crustal rocks such as granite. Each isotope goes through a series of decays to various elements, but the end products are stable isotopes of lead (Pb). ^{238}U decays to ^{206}Pb with a half-life of 4.5 billion years, and ^{235}U decays to ^{207}Pb with a half-life of 0.71 billion years. Nearly all the lead in use by humans is a product of some type of radioactive decay. The availability of two U-Pb decay systems makes a cross-check possible, for if analysis of each system yields the same date, accuracy and a closed system may be assumed.

Potassium to Argon   Most of the potassium (K) in such common minerals as some micas and feldspars is stable. With 19 protons, the isotopes with 20 and 22 neutrons (^{39}K and ^{41}K) make up all but some 0.01 percent of the potassium in the earth's crust. The isotope with 21 neutrons, ^{40}K, is unstable and decays in two ways. About 89 percent changes by beta emission, thus gaining a proton. The produced element with 20 protons is calcium and is no different than nonradioactively produced Ca. This part of the K decay system is therefore of scant use since some of the detected Ca might have been in the mineral at time zero. The remaining 11 percent of ^{40}K decays, not by emission, but by the nucleus capturing one of the electrons from an inner electron shell. This negative charge unites with a positively charged proton to form a neutron. Then, with only 18 protons, the potassium has become argon. The rate of decay of this 11 percent of the parent K is about 1.3 billion years, but care must be taken in the choice of the minerals and rock to be dated. Since argon is an inert gas, it does not combine chemically with other elements and can easily escape. If it does, any calculated date would be too young. If reheating of the rock is suspected, the possibility that the system has been opened to daughter escape must be considered.

Other Time Indicators   There are other radioactive decay systems used to tell time, but all are relatively similar to those already discussed. It is possible to get back a few thousand years in time by studying tree rings or yearly layers of sediments in certain types of former lakes. However, the most common method of dealing with the more recent past, prior to written records, is by comparing the amounts of two forms of carbon in what once were living things.

Radiocarbon dating involves an isotope of carbon that is in continual creation. The earth is constantly bombarded by nuclear particles, mostly protons, which come from outside the solar system. These particles often strike molecules of gases in the atmosphere. Secondarily, other particles are then produced. Many of these are neutrons, which in turn collide with other molecules of gas. When nitrogen, the most common gas in our atmosphere, is struck by a neutron, it emits a proton. The element with one less proton than nitrogen (which has seven) is carbon. This isotope of carbon has eight neutrons and is known as carbon 14. The most common kind of carbon has only six neutrons, is therefore carbon 12, and is stable. These forms of carbon are more or less evenly distributed at the surface of earth as atmospheric mixing occurs, but the stable ^{12}C outnumbers the unstable ^{14}C by about 1 trillion to 1. Atmospheric carbon is predominantly in combination with oxygen to form carbon dioxide (CO_2, the fourth most abundant gas). Plants use CO_2 in photosynthesis, taking it in during the day, and the carbon becomes part of their tissue. Animals eat plants, eat other animals that ate plants, or drink CO_2-bearing water, and so the carbon is distributed in all the organisms of earth. With the constancy of cellular renewal, the 1-trillion-to-1 ratio between carbon 12 and carbon 14 is closely maintained in living organisms, even though some ^{14}C is continually decaying back to nitrogen. Upon death and the cessation of carbon intake, the ratio begins to change. The longer ago the death, the less ^{14}C in relation to the stable ^{12}C will be found. Bones, wood, shells, and teeth may thus be dated. With a half-life of only 5730 years, ^{14}C allows relatively young organic remains that range from 500 to 50,000 years old to be dated. In material older than 50,000 years, or about nine half-lives, there is such a small amount of the originally minor ^{14}C present that it cannot be measured accurately. There are problems such as the contamination of buried material by the roots of modern plants, or possible fluctuations in the density of cosmic ray bombardment. Corrections for the latter have been made to cover the last few thousands of years, and even the cotton wrappings of ancient mummies can be dated within a few decades of the known reign of the wearer. On the other hand, the authenticity of a violin possibly made by Mr. Stradivari about the year 1700 cannot be determined. Not enough time has passed to make the changed ratio of the carbon isotopes in wood cut in the seventeenth or eighteenth century measurable with consistency.

CONCLUSIONS CONCERNING TIME

The periods of the geologic time scale (Figure 5-1) would be quite familiar to a geologist of 1896, when radioactivity first became known. It is only the numbers that isotopic decay systems have provided. Sedimentary strata and their fossils, most used to formulate the time scale, are normally not datable by radiometric means. This is unfortunate, since they make up the bulk of exposed rocks. Since the particles comprising a sedimentary rock may have weathered from rocks which crystallized hundreds of millions of years before, an age date on these particles gives the age of the original rock rather than the time of sedimentary deposition. Lava flows associated with fossil-bearing strata, crosscutting dikes, and other igneous-sedimentary associations have provided the link between fossil ages and real time in years.

Beginning with the concepts of uniformitarianism in the eighteenth century, the science of geology began to develop along modern lines. A few men put together models for the physical and organic evolution of earth. They based these on careful observation of things which were there for anyone to look at and see, but they had the ability to expand what they saw into grand concepts. They used the observations of others, but they unified the parts into the whole and made bold breakaways from their contemporaries' ideas of time. The eighteenth century geologist James Hutton, who is credited with the development of the uniformitarian concept (Chapter 2), was described as having such an acute awareness of time that "he could foretell in a running stream the final doom of a continent." First the geologists, later the biologists, and finally the physicists, have given mankind one of the most fundamental realizations in history: that of the passage of vast amounts of time. This realization has been fundamental to our ideas about the earth and the place of the human race in its organic realm.

SIX

ORIGINS

The universe as we know it seems to be made up of large groupings of matter known as galaxies (Figure 6-1). Our galaxy has about 100 billion stars, and there are billions of galaxies. One of the most startling observations of all time was that all these star groups seem to be flying away from each other, and modern estimates are that they began to do this some 13 billion years ago. This has led to an hypothesis of the creation of the universe appropriately known as the *big bang*. This present expansion may, according to one idea, go on forever. An alternative is that gravitational forces will some day prevail, cause all this matter to come back to its origin, becoming then a small, enormously dense mass, whereupon another "bang" sends it all outward again. Each cycle is thought to be about 100 billion years in length, and if so, it is speculative how many have passed and how many will occur.

Some astronomers assert that all stages in the birth, development, and death of star systems are present and visible in space. If this is true, perhaps the universe is in a state of continuous creation and destruction. New stars form from the debris of old ones. Astronomers have recognized some areas in space that impede the passage of light from behind them. These cold "clouds" are thought to be composed mainly of dispersed hydrogen. If enough of the hydrogen and other gaseous molecules is forced into aggregation by the pressure of light, their gravitational attractions may become sufficient to cause the cloud to contract and begin rotation. Rotation of mass seems to be a fundamental property of celestial bodies, whether

Figure 6-1 A spiral galaxy, similar in shape to our own. This is Messier 81 in Ursa Major, photographed with a 200-inch telescope. *(Courtesy of Hale Observatories.)*

planets or galaxies. As gravitational energy converts to heat and the pressures increase, fusion of hydrogen can begin, and as a consequence heat and light are released to space. Many centers of contraction may develop, each becoming a star. Rotation of the entire star mass increases and a galaxy is formed. It is thought that after billions of years, helium, the product of hydrogen fusion, builds up in its interior and the star begins to run out of its hydrogen fuel. As the core contracts and heat builds up, even the previously inactive helium atoms begin merging and form carbon and other elements. More energy is released in this process, more and heavier elements form, and finally the star's energy is gone. The nuclei can contract no more and the star may cool. Even then the larger stars may still emit atomic particles to space, causing additional shrinkage and renewed heating. After a long period of quiescence the temperatures may build up to billions of degrees. At that stage the star explodes and a supernova comes into being. Its debris, along with hydrogen in space, may form the material for new stars to begin. Supernovae have occurred within our own galaxy on several occasions within history, but none since the telescope was invented.

Our sun, medium in size, has sufficient hydrogen to produce energy at its current rate for tens of billions of years. However, the gravitational pressures on the increasing amounts of helium in the sun's core will cause temperatures to rise, forcing other nuclear reactions and consuming the hydrogen much earlier. In 5 or 6 billion years the earth will be too hot for liquid water to exist.

ORIGIN OF THE SOLAR SYSTEM

Toward the outskirts of our galaxy, one of its billions of stars, our sun, has a planetary system. How did the planets come into existence? Most astronomers now think that when this star began to form, the centrifugal forces of rotation caused some debris to move outward from the central area. Before the beginning of hydrogen fusion, rings of matter formed on the outskirts of the protostar and gravitational forces caused several centers of self-compression. Spacial debris, such as frozen gases and meteorites, was gravitationally collected by these centers, which were apparently much larger in size than the planets they were to become. All this is thought to have occurred in darkness and at low temperatures. These embryonic planets must have had much the same composition as the protosun; only a small percentage of their mass was made up of the heavier elements, which perhaps were given off by a distant supernova. As the sun contracted and its fusion began, light, heat, and subatomic particles were emitted. The solar wind of particles swept the planets clear of much of their gaseous envelopes. The planets themselves were warmed by solar radiation and, hundreds of millions of years later, all that remained on those close to the sun were the heavier elements. Those farther away were able to retain some of their lighter atmospheric components.

In the case of earth, the various elements had, during all this time, been segregating themselves. The heavier elements gravitated inward toward the core. If the accretion and gravitational collapsing of earth took place fairly rapidly, then enough energy would have been released to cause melting. Earth's nickel and iron core would have formed very early, probably only hundreds of millions of years after the initial cold formation of the proto-planet. An alternative hypothesis is that accretion took place more slowly and segregation of heavier elements toward the core was not accompanied by melting. In this model, the heat buildup from energy released by the radioactive decay of elements, mainly uranium and thorium, produced a phase of melting essentially secondary to the earth's formation. Radioactive heat is, of course, still being produced, although at a rate much lower than early in earth's history since so much radioactive matter has already decayed.

If and when melting occurred and iron concentrated in the core, the lightest materials floated outward, cooled, and formed the early crust. This crustal matter must have formed at least 3.8 billion years ago since we know of rocks that age. On the basis of age determinations of meteorites and some moon rocks, the solar system, and hence earth too, probably formed about 4.5 or 4.6 billion years ago.

There is no model of the formation of the solar system that satisfies all the valid questions about its current state, much less all the questioners. There is general agreement that at least most of our planets formed along with our sun, that protoearth formed by the gravitational attraction of essentially cold matter, and that earth at one time became much hotter than it now is.

ORIGIN OF THE CRUST

The crust of the earth is a very small part of its total mass. The continental portion, covering about 35 percent of the surface, is fundamentally granitic in overall composition and very different from the ultramafic mantle beneath. Oceanic crust is chemically similar to the upper mantle, and its creation is a present problem rather than an historic one. The present and nearly continu-ous creation of oceanic crust is the main thesis of sea-floor spreading and plate tectonics. The origin of the continental portion of the crust is fairly easy to speculate on, for no glaring problems exist. When the mantle was molten 4 or 5 billion years ago, fractional crystallization allowed the lighter material to segregate and move up to the surface. A magma of mantle type composition can yield several percent of granitic fraction, and the continental crust has less than 1 percent of the mantle's volume. Separation of the continental crustal fraction may still be occurring, but the rate must be far slower because the mantle is probably considerably cooler than it once was. With the higher radiogenic heat of the past, early granitic fractions probably remelted and resegregated repeatedly, but for at least 3.8 billion years some crustal matter has persisted.

ORIGIN OF OCEANS

The oceanic crust, thinner and of a higher density than continental crust, would form a basin even if no oceanic waters existed. Why? Because of isostasy, which you studied in Chapter 3. But the ocean floor would not be as low as it is now (an average of nearly 5000 meters below the average elevation of continental crust), for the weight of 4000 meters of water does depress the oceanic crust somewhat.

Earlier concepts of the origin of our liquid water commonly involved a vaporous envelope around a hot earth, finally condensing and falling as rain when the earth cooled. There are several lines of investigation that put strong restraints on any such event. For example, the earth is quite deficient, compared to cosmic norms, of several elements such as neon. This gas probably was present in normal abundance during the early accretion but was swept from the planet when our sun began radiating energy. Water has about the same molecular weight as neon, and it too would have been swept off the early planet.

The liquid water of earth probably came from its interior. The oxygen and hydrogen were originally bonded to minerals and became free to combine as partial melting occurred. As the light water vapor was carried to the surface, much may have escaped from the earth, but as the surface became cool enough for the crust to be maintained, accumulation began. A melt of overall granitic composition commonly contains over 2 percent water, and so the idea of water being derived by *outgassing* from magmas is quite compatible with modern observations.

Modern volcanism provides some opportunities for studying outgassing. Isotopic studies show that most of the water vapor in volcanic gases was incorporated into the magma from surficial (rain) water which worked its way underground, but a small proportion of the water vapor is thought to be from the deeper interior. Since some water is carried down beneath the crust in subduction zones, either between mineral grains or within mineral structures, there is now a cyclic system in operation.

Sediments laid down in what were apparently large bodies of water have been dated at well over 3 billion years. The oceans were probably smaller at first, but there is no definite indication that radical volume changes have occurred in the last hundreds of millions of years. The two principal ions in seawater, chlorine and sodium, have undoubtedly been in the oceanic system almost from the beginning. Chlorine is another product of outgassing, and sodium is carried to the seas as a by-product of chemical weathering of rock. The latter process must have begun as soon as liquid water and rock met on the crust of the earth.

ORIGIN OF THE EARLY ATMOSPHERE

Several lines of geochemical and geophysical data lead to the conclusion that earth's present atmosphere, about 78 percent nitrogen and 21 percent oxygen, is very different from any very early one. The lack of hydrogen, helium, and other gases of low atomic weight, which are common elsewhere in the solar system, is explicable; before the pre-earth materials had aggregated into one dense mass, the gravitational attraction of the scattered materials was too low to retain the light gases. The heavier gases, neon for example, were probably removed somewhat later by the solar wind of subatomic particles radiating from our sun. When the earth finally reached a mass concentration large enough to provide sufficient gravitational force, outgassing components began to be retained. As the sun began to emit more heat energy with time, earth's lighter gases may have continued to escape to space from the early atmosphere.

The nature of the first, more-or-less-retainable atmosphere is debatable. In addition to water vapor, several components—principally nitrogen, methane, ammonia, carbon dioxide, and perhaps hydrogen—were probably present. Their percentages are debatable, but most scientists agree that free oxygen was not there in any significant quantity.

There is one way that free oxygen could have begun to form. Water vapor will dissociate if exposed to enough ultraviolet radiation. Today the surface is shielded from excessive uv radiation by a layer of ozone (O_3) in the upper atmosphere. Since free oxygen is thought not to have existed, more must have penetrated the atmospheric envelop in the past. This caused the water to break down as follows: $H_2O + uv \rightarrow H_2 + O$. By such a process, we can imagine our atmospheric oxygen building up to present levels. However, there are several constraints on this model. One is the presence of unoxidized minerals containing iron and uranium in early Precambrian sedimentary rocks; if early oxygen had been present, these minerals would have readily combined with the oxygen. Another constraint, even more difficult to bypass, is that free oxygen in quantity would have broken down any complex organic molecules that formed in the primitive oceans and prevented the development of life. Oxygen is necessary for most life on earth, but plants and animals must produce enzymes to mediate its destructive effect on their organic compounds.

In the system described above it is thought that the dissociation of water would have been self-limiting. As oxygen was produced, free ions would combine to O_2 and O_3. The ozone thus produced would act as a shield to ultraviolet penetration, as it does now, and prevent further dissociation. This so-called shadow effect may be understood by an analogy. If sunlight grew hair on a head by a reaction with skin, a hairless head would have a rapid growth. But as the product of the reaction, hair, became abundant, it would shield the skin from light penetration. So hair could grow only so much before it, itself, limited its production. Some calculations have indicated that the self-limiting effects of oxygen production by photodissociation would have permitted less than 1 percent of the present level of oxygen to accumulate in an early atmosphere. This state of affairs probably existed during the first 1 to 2 billion years of earth history.

ORIGIN OF LIFE AND AN OXYGEN ATMOSPHERE

In 1953, S. L. Miller, a graduate student at the University of Chicago, carried out a now-classical experiment. On the assumptions that the early earth had an essentially oxygen-free atmosphere consisting of water, hydrogen, methane (CH_4), and ammonia (NH_3), and that temperatures were less than the boiling point of water, he simulated these conditions (Figure 6-2). Using an electric spark for energy, the experiment ran for about 140 hours. At the end of this time, the H_2O, H_2, and CH_4 and NH_3 combination had been altered and,

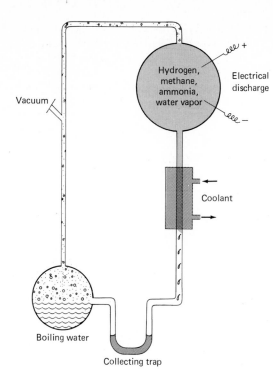

Figure 6-2 Diagram of the apparatus used by S. L. Miller in his 1953 experiment. The gases of hydrogen, methane, ammonia, and water vapor (simulating an early-earth atmosphere) were subjected to electric sparks as an energy source. Amino acids, the fundamental building blocks of proteins, formed.

in addition to the gases of carbon monoxide, carbon dioxide, and nitrogen, amino acids had been produced. Amino acids, in combination, form the proteins which are a fundamental component in the structure of all plants and animals. Since then, many similar experiments, with various sources of energy thought to have been available on earth, and using several atmospheric combinations, have been conducted. A large number of complex organic molecules have been produced, including at least 16 essential amino acids, peptides, sugars, nucleotides, and even ATP, the energy source used in cells to synthesize proteins. One factor was common to all these syntheses of organic matter from inorganic matter: if free oxygen was present as part of the experimental atmosphere, it *prevented* the formation of these complex large organic molecules.

On the early earth, in the absence of free oxygen in significant quantities, the sea could have become a "broth" of organic molecules. The forces of intermolecular attraction can cause segregation of some molecules into aggregates which differ in their composition from their surroundings. These droplets, known as *coacervates*, may develop an outer membrane which acts as a selective absorption barrier to molecules from the surrounding medium. Some of these aggregates can be thought of as "competing" for raw materials, growing at the expense of others. A form of natural selection may have been occurring before recognizable life forms appeared. From this state of affairs, which can be examined experimentally, to an aggregation of material which has the ability to mutate, to synthesize molecules like itself, and to transmit inheritable qualities to daughter aggregates as it splits is not a difficult mental jump, but that jump is over a broad area of the unknown. It has not, as yet, been accomplished in a laboratory. These hypothetical units, probably composed of proteins and nucleic acids, may have had some of the characteristics of free genes, or perhaps of a virus. All known viruses are parasitic, but free-living ones would be difficult to detect. The most basic and primitive free-living life forms we know of are *bacteria* and *blue-green algae*. These have no membranated cell nucleus or discrete grouping of their chromosomes. Other criteria separate them from other organisms, but although they are considered to be primitive, they are nevertheless highly complex life forms.

The earliest direct evidence of life on earth is in the form of what may be bacterial and blue-green algal cells in rocks over 3 billion years old. Blue-green algae are photosynthetic and produce free oxygen: $CO_2 + H_2O \xrightarrow{\text{light}}$ carbohydrate $+ O_2$. Figure 6-3 illustrates some cells, possibly of blue-green algae, from rocks nearly 2 billion years old. By this time, much of the oxygen produced earlier by algae had probably fulfilled the role of oxidizing certain inorganic compounds. For example, most of the world's major iron-ore deposits are in the form of iron oxides. These deposits are usually within the age range of 1.8 to 2.0 billion years old and may have formed as free oxygen became available and caused the oxidation and precipitation of iron compounds which previously were soluble and had built up in the seas. By about 2 billion years ago it seems that photosynthetically produced oxygen began to accumulate in the atmosphere, and probably by the end of Precambrian time, 600 million years ago, had built up toward present levels. Today, free oxygen seems to be in a state of reasonable balance between its production by algae and other plants and its inorganic and organic consumption, the latter by respiration in both plants and animals.

The origin of life and, at least on earth, the evolution of an oxygen-rich atmosphere seem to have been an almost inevitable process. With the vast numbers of planets thought likely to exist in the universe, it seems improbable that only earth possesses life. Whether life on other planets is completely unlike ours or whether it may have inevitable similarities is theoretical. Messages have been sent out from earth, but listeners for corresponding signals from outside our solar system haven't been rewarded yet.

APPEARANCE OF ANIMALS

The end of the Precambrian era, some 600 million years ago, is recorded by the appearance of abundant fossils of complex animals. After 4000 million years of time some biochemical events occurred which allowed the preservation of ancient life and caused geologists to draw a nomenclatural boundary. Cambrian strata are characterized by their fossils; nothing else distinguishes these strata from some Precambrian sedimentary sequences. Among the many forms of life which are known from the earliest Cambrian-age rocks, trilobites are the most abundant as species. These animals, commonly a few inches long, segmented, with legs, and usually with eyes and other sensory

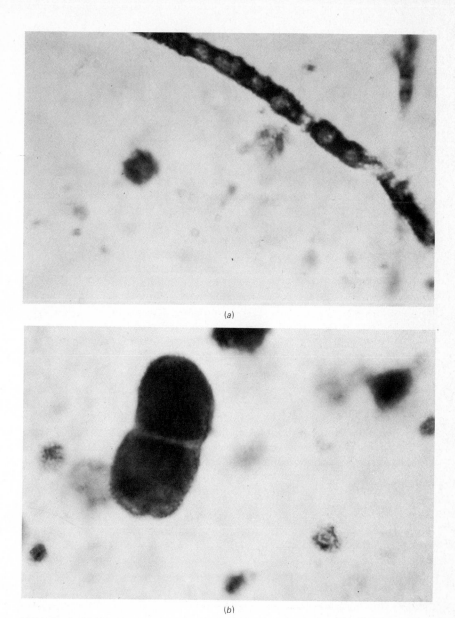

(a)

(b)

Figure 6-3 Photomicrographs of a cell chain and a dividing spherical cell found in rocks nearly 2 billion years old from North America. Both are possibly blue-green algae.

organs, are complicated and must have had a long, long evolutionary history (Figure 6-4).

Unicellular animal-type organisms are abundant today, and one is apt to

Figure 6-4   A fossil trilobite from the Cambrian Period. *(Courtesy of R. Sloan.)*

think the earliest animals were also one-celled. But the rare finds of fossil cells in rocks of Precambrian age have not shed much light on the nature of the first animals. In Australia, impressions of soft-bodied animals that lived in upper Precambrian time, about 670 million years ago, have been found. They are now the oldest unquestionable evidence of animals. Finds of similar organisms have been made on other continents, but in all cases these fossils are of very advanced animal forms.

The reason for the Cambrian revolution in life is probably that some change in physical conditions produced a change in the natural selection of organisms. The biological and physical evolution of the earth are quite intertwined. Precambrian sedimentary rocks are often a record of the shallow continental seas of that time. These seas would seem to have been the likely places for abundant life, as those of later times were. Full of light, nutrients, and photosynthesing organisms, they would seem to be an animal's paradise. They may have been, and probably the only reason these organisms are unknown to us is that they lacked hard parts capable of easy fossilization. Until the very late Precambrian, even trails and tracks are nearly unknown in the strata. Bottom dwellers of large size seem to have been absent. A shell can be a valuable thing for a clam or snail or other invertebrate. For instance, it provides protection from a changing environment and gives support for muscles to allow locomotion in the search for food. But it is not so valuable to an organism that must live near the water's surface, for it does weigh. The Cambrian era marks the time when organisms developed the ability to produce a hardened exoskeleton, or shell. This ability probably developed in

TIME (in billions of years ago)	
CAMBRIAN	Worldwide occurrence of hard-shelled animals. (Trilobites and brachiopods principal fossils.)
0.6	End of Precambrian era.
0.67	Approximate age of first known animals: soft-bodied corals?, jellyfish, worms, etc. (complexity of forms indicates a long prehistory).
1.0	Earliest known advanced cell type: green algae (probably appeared much earlier).
	Evolution of animals. Photosynthetic activity of marine unicellular plants causing oxygen levels in atmosphere to begin approach to modern levels. Ultraviolet protective ozone layer developing.
2.0	Approximate age of oldest well-preserved fossils, photo-synthetic blue-green algae. Initial O_2 production going into minerals (e.g., ferrous iron to ferric iron—major iron ore formations 1.8–2.8 b.y.), then into atmosphere. Abiologic spontaneous generation of organic compounds becoming impossible owing to free oxygen buildup.
3.0	Evolution of photosynthetic organisms. Approximate age of evidence of first life: algal structures in rocks (stromatolites); possible bacteria and blue-green algae.
3.5	Evolution of first organisms. Outgassing continues and atmosphere develops (? CO_2, CO, N_2, SO_2—possibly some H_2, CH_4, NH_3 ?). "Oceans" with buildup of abiologically produced complex organic molecules (amino acids, peptides, nucleic acids, ATP, etc.) via ultraviolet energy, etc., and atmospheric components. Coacervates forming? Fermentation most probable metabolic energy process.
3.8	Approximate age of oldest known earth rocks. Outgassing from interior building up a reducing atmosphere (? CH_4 NH_3, N_2, H_2 ?) and "oceans." Probable loss of some atmospheric components to space.
4.6	Probable age of Earth and other planets. Evidence: Radio-isotope age dating of meteorites and lunar rocks; amounts and ratios of terrestrial lead isotopes. Earth differentiating into core, mantle; crust begins forming. No physical data.

Figure 6-5 Approximate times in the early development of life. Read from bottom up.

response to changes which made the sea bottom a hospitable environment. These changes may have been both biological and physical. Perhaps oxygen finally became abundant enough to saturate the bottom waters or perhaps some chemical event tied to rates of sea-floor spreading and magma production occurred in the seas. Whatever the causes, the development of hard shells and other exoskeletons was an event of great magnitude, and fully justifies the geologists honoring their appearance by erecting an era boundary for this point in time (Figure 6-5).

SEVEN

THE LONG PRECAMBRIAN—
THE FIRST SEVEN-EIGHTHS OF EARTH'S HISTORY

There is an old Finnish proverb—"Nothing is so plentiful as time." That statement is especially applicable to the Precambrian, for it encompasses geologic time from earth's distant beginnings an estimated 4.5 billion years (4.5 b.y.) ago up to about 600 million years ago, when fossils first became abundant. However, the oldest date obtained on rocks so far is about 3.8 b.y. on rocks from southwestern Minnesota and Greenland. Obviously, the very length of the Precambrian is itself sufficient to make the study of Precambrian rocks worthwhile in terms of interpreting earth's history. But there are two other very important reasons for studying these old rocks: 20 percent of earth's land area has Precambrian rocks at the surface, and Precambrian rocks provide us with a substantial percentage of our mineral wealth.

PRECAMBRIAN SHIELDS

Each continent has a Precambrian nucleus, or shield (Figure 7-1), so named because of the resemblance of these regions to a warrior's shield lying on the ground, lower on the outer edges and slightly higher in the center. Geologically younger rocks essentially surround each shield and lap up onto it. The shields have been the sites of volcanism, deformation, intrusion, uplift, mountain building, and probably any other geologic process one can think of. For at least the last 600 m.y., however, they have been stable, geologically

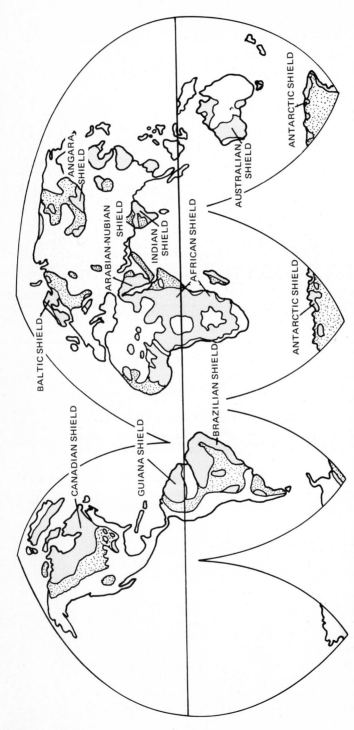

Figure 7-1 Precambrian shields of the world, shown in gray. The dotted areas signify places where the shields are buried under a thin cover of sedimentary rocks. The white areas are largely younger rocks.

Figure 7-2   Aerial view of part of the Canadian Shield. Note the lack of relief, the result of billions of years of relative stability and erosion. The lakes are glacial features.

quiet areas largely above sea level and therefore have been subjected to erosion ("tear-it-down" processes) without the violent "build-it-up" processes such as mountain building to offset the erosion. However, as erosion proceeds, isostatic balance is maintained and the shields stay above sea level. Consequently, the shields today are generally low-lying, deeply eroded, comparatively featureless regions (Figure 7-2).

Let's look more closely at the shield closest to us, the Canadian Shield (Figure 7-3). It is even larger than it looks in the figure, for Precambrian rocks underlie younger rocks adjacent to the shield and poke through the younger rocks at many other localities in North America including the bottom of the Grand Canyon and in the cores of many mountain ranges.

THE STUDY OF PRECAMBRIAN ROCKS

Precambrian rocks have generally been the least studied of all rocks. Professor C. W. Holmes of England made a neat analogy. He compared all geologic history to a six-story building under construction. Each story is 600 m.y. high. A human being is standing on the roof of the building, and the top floor is nearly completed. However, the bottom five floors have only the superstructure completed; nearly everything else remains to be filled in. And a few decades ago when he presented this picture he predicted that we may even have to put a basement under our building before we're done. We've started digging it already, with dates as old as 3.8 b.y.

Why aren't the lower five floors, the Precambrian floors, occupied? If they are as important as we've said, what's the problem? Actually, there are

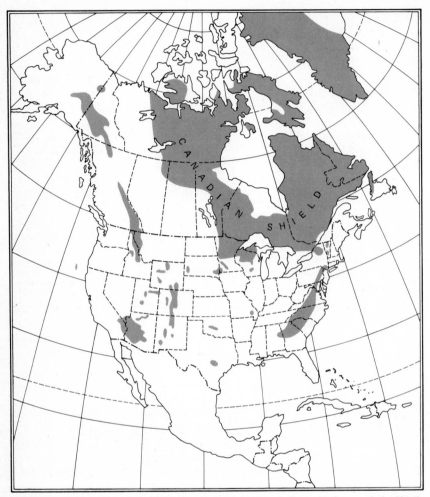

Figure 7-3 The Canadian Shield and other areas of Precambrian rock in North America. The patch of white on the shield adjacent to Hudson's Bay is a thin cover of younger rocks upon the Precambrian.

many problems. Rather than identify all the problems, we can lump them together and say that the rocks are "messy" and they are essentially unfossiliferous. Usually, the older the Precambrian rocks, the more events they have been through during their history. Some rocks have been folded, faulted, intruded, and metamorphosed several times, and each such event tends to obscure the previous events a bit more.

Although some fossils have been found in Precambrian rocks (Figure 6-3), the Precambrian strata are essentially unfossiliferous. Without fossils, correlation (showing the same age relationship) until quite recently had to be made on the basis of the rock types present. This was risky, to say the least, for we already know from Chapter 2 that rock types differ from place to place. An example of an attempted correlation was one made by A. C. Lawson, one of the great earlier Precambrian geologists of North America. While with the Geological Survey of Canada, he studied granites near the St. Lawrence River, appropriately naming them *Laurentian granites*. In the late 1800s, he observed very similar granites in the Ontario-Minnesota border area and called them Laurentian as well. In recent years, radiometric age dating has shown his original Laurentian rocks to be about 1.0 b.y. old and those in Ontario-Minnesota to be 2.7 b.y. old! This example also serves to illustrate that radiometric age dating is especially valuable to geologists working with the unfossiliferous Precambrian.

Radiometric dates for the rocks of the Canadian Shield and other Precambrian rocks in North America seem to form a crudely concentric pattern (Figure 7-4) with the oldest in the center and younger Precambrian rocks on the outer edges. The ages are largely from igneous rocks and therefore represent major times of intrusion and/or volcanism. If all rocks,

Figure 7-4 Radiometric-age provinces of the Precambrian of North America. Dates are generalized; older or younger dates can be present in each province.

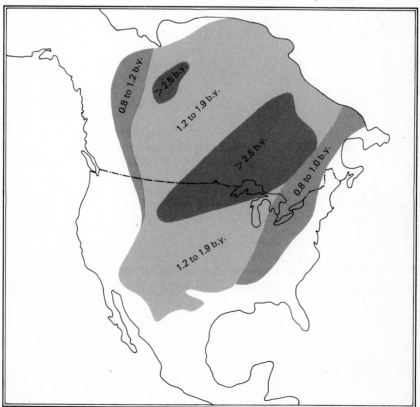

including sedimentary and metamorphic, could be dated, the dates might form a more continuous spectrum between 3.8 and 0.6 b.y. ago.

There are several subdivisions of the Precambrian in use; the United States Geologic Survey uses *x*, *y*, and *z* and the Geological Survey of Canada has a number of names for rocks of different ages. For the purposes of this generalized discussion, we prefer to use early Precambrian for that section of time older than 2.5 b.y., middle Precambrian for 1.2 to 2.5 b.y., and late Precambrian for the time from 0.6 to 1.2 b.y. ago.

EARLY PRECAMBRIAN TIME

Determining the geological history of a sequence of rocks is a goal of most geological investigators. In the late 1800s and early 1900s, considerable time was spent searching for the "original" granitic crust, which all geologists assumed must exist if the earth had a hot, molten origin (the prevailing theory of that time). But whenever they found granites, the granites were intruding *older* sedimentary and volcanic rocks (Figure 7-5). Essentially, that is the status of the problem today, too. Figure 7-6 shows a portion of the oldest part of the Canadian Shield, that is largely composed of granitic rocks with belts of sedimentary and volcanic rocks which are all older than the granitic rocks.

Figure 7-5 (*a*) Lower Precambrian granites (light-colored) dated at about 2.7 b.y. cutting across older, darker, metamorphosed volcanic rocks in Ontario. Note geologist for scale. (*b*) (opposite page) Granite injected into beds of metamorphosed sedimentary rock (now biotite schist) in Minnesota; both rocks have been highly deformed. (*c*) (opposite page) Lower Precambrian conglomerate in Minnesota which has been squeezed and stretched. Note that most pebbles are elongated parallel to the length of the photograph, but that the light-colored granite pebbles have retained their original shapes.

(*a*)

(b)

(c)

Figure 7-5 continued

Figure 7-6 Portion of the Canadian Shield north of Lake Superior. The lower Precambrian metamorphosed volcanic and sedimentary belts are shown in gray, the blank areas represent younger but still lower Precambrian granitic rocks which intruded the belts about 2.7 b.y. ago, and the dotted areas represent middle and upper Precambrian rocks. *(After F. J. Pettijohn, 1943, courtesy of Geological Society of America Bulletin.)*

But sedimentary and volcanic rocks have to be deposited *on* something, so what was the original basement? Granite is still a good guess, and another good guess is basalt, like the present oceanic crust. Whichever it was, it has probably been largely destroyed by the intrusion of the large granitic bodies.

Yet detailed studies in just the last few years have resulted in the discovery of rocks a billion years older (3.5 to 3.8 b.y. old) than were known a decade ago (Figure 7-7). These oldest rocks are gneisses, schists, and amphibolites, which are metamorphic rocks which were probably once largely volcanic rocks. So even if such older rocks are the "basement" rocks upon which the younger (2.7 b.y. old) volcanic-sedimentary rocks were deposited, they themselves needed a basement of some sort to be deposited upon.

The abundant granites of the shields may have formed from the melting of earlier sedimentary and volcanic rocks, from the partial melting of mantle material, or perhaps even by a remelting of original granitic crust. Problems! And interestingly, most of these granites have been dated at about 2.7 b.y. ago; it seems that there may have been a worldwide magmatic event (melting) at that time in history. Perhaps the accumulated heat of radioactive decay attained a threshold value and melted existing rocks. (Because radioactive isotopes decay with time, they would have been more abundant in the early Precambrian and would have provided more radiogenic heat than they now do.)

Rocks in the Precambrian volcanic-sedimentary belts are commonly as much as 10,000 meters thick and consist of basalt flows (commonly pillowed, as in Figure 3-4, indicative of deposition under water), abundant intermediate to felsic pyroclastic volcanic rocks representing explosive volcanism, and abundant sedimentary rocks, many which appear to be derived from the erosion of the volcanic piles. Turbidity currents appear to have carried much of the sediment off these volcanic centers. All these rocks have been faulted and folded. Most beds are now steeply dipping or vertical and metamorphosed during deformation and intrusion of the granite rocks (Figure 7-5). The steep inclinations of the layered rocks suggest that they once projected high into the air; mountains of at least moderate size were probably common

Figure 7-7 A view of the ancient gneisses (banded metamorphic rocks) in the Minnesota River Valley of southwestern Minnesota. Similar rocks in the valley have been dated at 3.8 b.y. *(Courtesy of J. A. Grant.)*

over the old part of the shield. Today, we are seeing only erosional remnants of these deformed belt rocks.

Many gold, silver, copper, zinc, and lead deposits occur in these belts of volcanic and sedimentary rocks in Canada, especially in the volcanic portions where the metals appear to have been concentrated by volcanic processes. And geologists are now asking whether these volcanic-sedimentary belts, which appear to be somewhat similar to present-day volcanic island arcs such as Japan or the Philippines, might not have been located near plate boundaries, like these modern areas. Thus, another application of uniformitarianism. However, there are indications that some early Precambrian granitic bodies were intruded at shallow depths into the volcanic piles and were rapidly exposed and eroded. Yet younger granites appear to have cooled at moderate depths. For reasons which we cannot go into here, it seems likely that in early Precambrian time, the earth's crust, whatever it was composed of, was much thinner than the present crust. It appears to have been hotter as well, owing to heat generated by radioactivity in the upper mantle and lower crust. If these two things were true, then the basic physical environment during the formation of early Precambrian rocks was different than today's environment. If so, the principle of uniformitarianism must be applied with caution.

MIDDLE PRECAMBRIAN TIME
During middle Precambrian time, many sequences of rocks were formed which are much like many younger rocks. For example, cross-bedded and ripple-marked quartz-rich sandstones, the result of long reworking of sediment in shallow waters, became relatively common. Limestones, rare in the early Precambrian, appear more commonly. Even ancient (2.1 to 2.4 b.y. old) glacial deposits (lithified tills, outwash deposits, and varves) occur north of Lake Huron and elsewhere (Figure 7-8). Geosynclines, with miogeosynclinal and eugeosynclinal portions, are well developed, as in Labrador.

The middle Precambrian rocks are also quite unique in that they contain most of the world's large iron deposits, mainly hematite (Fe_2O_3), deposited as sedimentary rocks (Figure 2-35). The exact chemistry of their origin is a problem, for iron-rich rocks are not being formed today. It seems that oxygen had become sufficiently abundant sometime about 1.9 b.y. ago to combine with dissolved iron and form the iron oxides. The presence of abundant oxygen, as you learned in the previous chapter, is linked with life in the sea. Similarly, red beds, sedimentary rocks colored red by a minor amount of hematite, also became abundant at about that same point in time. Thus, the iron oxide minerals became a sink, or trap, for oxygen. (Today, the iron oxides, the calcium carbonate (CO_3) minerals, and the sulfate (SO_4) minerals contain more than 90 percent of the earth's total oxygen.) From that time on, about 1.9 b.y. ago, oxygen became more abundant in the atmosphere.

In the Lake Superior region and in Labrador, the middle Precambrian sequence of rocks consists of, in order, quartzites (representing about half a billion years of weathering and erosion), followed by iron formation

Figure 7-8   Middle Precambrian glacial tillite in Ontario, north of Lake Huron. The boulders are mostly granite, in a matrix of mud and sand. Such poor sorting is characteristic of glacial ice deposits. *(Courtesy of Bevan Alwin.)*

(representing the widespread oxidation of dissolved iron), followed by graywackes, mudstones, and local volcanics (representing geosynclinal sedimentation). In the Lake Superior region, this period of sedimentation was followed by a rather poorly studied episode of mountain building, which occurred about 1.6 to 1.9 b.y. ago. It will suffice to say that mountains, now gone, were formed in central Minnesota, Wisconsin, and northern Michigan.

LATE PRECAMBRIAN TIME

Late Precambrian time is represented in the rock record by quartz sandstones, basalt flows and dikes, intrusive mafic rocks, including gabbroic rocks and rather unique plagioclase-rich rocks called anorthosites, and thick sequences of red beds (commonly conglomerates, feldspathic sandstones, siltstones, and shales).

The Lake Superior region has one of the best-studied rock sequences of late Precambrian age. The sequence from bottom to top consists of quartzites representing several hundred million years of weathering and erosion, an 8000-meter-thick, slightly tilted pile of dominantly basaltic lava flows (Figure 7-9) which formed a basaltic plateau on the present site of Lake Superior, a large gabbroic complex which intruded into the flows but which yields the same age dates as the flows (1.1 b.y.), and as much as several thousand

(a)

(b)

Figure 7-9 (a) Upper Precambrian lava flows, largely basaltic, on the north shore of Lake Superior. They are all dipping gently to the right, into the lake. (b) Closer view of flows and gas-bubble cavities which have been filled with minerals such as calcite, zeolite, and quartz. Fine-grained quartz in cavities, when banded, is called agate. The bottom half of the view is the top of a flow, with many filled cavities. The top half of the photo is the more massive bottom of younger flow.

meters of arkosic red beds which pass upward into quartz sandstones. The quartz sandstones, evidently the reworked product of the arkoses, are difficult to distinguish from overlying fossiliferous Cambrian sandstones.

Like the rocks formed during early and middle Precambrian time, the rocks of late Precambrian age also contain economic mineral deposits. The native metallic copper deposits of northern Michigan are unique deposits formed in porous lava flows and in interbedded conglomerates. At the White Pine Mine in northern Michigan fine copper minerals are currently being removed from a black shale unit. The Duluth gabbroic complex in northeastern Minnesota contains large reserves of low-grade copper and nickel minerals, and their development seems imminent.

A very interesting aspect of late Precambrian history relates to the source of the plateau basalts and the gabbroic complex. Such rocks are best known

Figure 7-10 The mid-continent gravity high is a zone of both higher gravity and higher magnetism. Both of these characteristics can be related to the heavy and relatively magnetic basalts and gabbros of the Lake Superior region; drill holes have also penetrated basalts beneath younger rocks at scattered points elsewhere along the high. It has been suggested that this large feature is the result of a rifting, or splitting, of the continent 1.1 b.y. ago. *(After C. G. Chase and T. H. Gilmer, 1973, Earth and Planetary Science Letters, vol. 21, pp. 70–78. Courtesy of Elsevier Scientific Publishing Co.)*

from the Lake Superior region, where they are well exposed; however, drill cores and gravity and magnetic measurements indicate a belt of basalts a few tens of kilometers wide extending from Lake Superior southwestward into Kansas (Figure 7-10). It has been suggested that this large feature represents a cracking of the crust 1.1 b.y. ago, similar to the geologically recent and still-continuing cracking, or rifting, in East Africa and similar to the rifting and breakup of Pangaea described in Chapter 3. But for some reason it stopped and North America did not open up and accommodate a new ocean. Too bad, for midcontinental cities—such as Thunder Bay, Ontario; Duluth, Minnesota; Des Moines, Iowa; and Omaha, Nebraska—missed the chance to be seaside cities.

CONCLUSIONS

We've said that the oldest age determinations on earth rocks are 3.8 b.y.; however, meteorites and some moon rocks have been interpreted to be 4.5 to 4.6 b.y. old. Perhaps we'll find older rocks on earth, in spite of the fact that the active earth with its weathering, volcanism, metamorphism, and deformation has made the chances rather slim.

The Precambrian rocks have yielded much information about the first seven-eighths of the earth's history, but much more remains to be learned. Although these old rocks do not readily give up their secrets, it is worth working on them until they do. Two of the best-hidden secrets to date are the origin of the early crust and the role, if any, which plate tectonics played during Precambrian time. The rewards of study can be great, in terms of both economics and academics.

EIGHT

THE ERAS OF LIFE

Fossils are common in the strata laid down in the seas which encroached upon the continents (epicontinental seas) after Precambrian time. When a plant or animal dies and is buried before its hard parts are destroyed, it may be preserved in the lithified sediments. Shales and limestones usually contain the better fossils because they are more commonly deposited in low-energy zones where wave action has not caused the breakup of shells or skeletons. Organisms that lived on land are less commonly fossilized since before they can be buried they are apt to be gnawed by scavengers and their hard parts are exposed to weathering and erosion. Rarely, organisms may be preserved in glacier ice for a few thousand years or get mired in a surface seep of viscous petroleum, or tar. The famous La Brea tar pits of California have yielded thousands of excellent specimens of animals that lived a few thousand years ago.

For the most part we are biased in our knowledge of past life, since the majority of the species we know of were marine bottom dwellers with shells or hardened exoskeletons, such as that of a lobster. About $1\frac{1}{2}$ million living species of plants and animals have been described and probably at least an equal number are yet to be described. We have described only about 130,000 species of organisms from rocks deposited during the last 600 million years, and we probably have knowledge of less than 1 percent of the life of the past.

As mentioned in Chapter 5, there are morphological changes in the organisms of a population as time progresses. These allow us to determine the geologic period during which sediment was deposited by studying the fossils in the sedimentary rock. The major boundaries of the geologic time scale (Figure 8-1), separating eras, signify major changes. These changes are most commonly biologic, but often widespread physical changes at the earth's surface are associated with them. On a never-changing earth, it would be doubtful if organic evolution would ever proceed; once a population of organisms became perfectly adapted to its environment, all changes in any individuals would be detrimental. The evolution of life forms is a perfectly natural result of life on an unstable planet. During all geologic time, various forms of life developed and became extinct. Most of these were offshoots of already-well-established major types, and probably no major large grouping (phylum) of animals has appeared that is not with us today (Figure 8-2).

In this chapter a few of the more common or, to us, more important life forms of the past will be described, era by era. But don't lose sight of the fact that life is and was a continuum, a complex continuum with immense variation.

THE PALEOZOIC ERA (600 TO 225 MILLION YEARS AGO)

Cambrian seas, at one time or another during the period, covered much of what is now North America. The evidence is the presence of the rock strata that originally were sediments deposited in those seas. Of course, some of the Cambrian strata were later eroded, as were those of all periods, and the exact extent and boundaries of epicontinental seas of the past are open to different interpretations. It is from these remaining deposits that our first *extensive* knowledge of life on earth is derived. The Cambrian may be described as the period in which the first abundant *fossilizable* organisms lived, but they are not a very diverse group. Trilobites (to become extinct at the end of the Paleozoic) and brachiopods (with us still) make up about 90 percent of the known Cambrian organisms (Figure 6-4). The shell material common to most known Cambrian organisms was fairly similar to that of a modern crab, and these hard parts permitted their legacy to be left. There were many species of both trilobites and brachiopods in the Cambrian seas, and they successfully adapted to life on the bottom and became widespread. Among the remaining 10 percent of the known Cambrian organisms are found the precursors of many forms of invertebrate animal life common to modern seas.

The Cambrian period is thought to have lasted about 100 million years, longer than any period since. During this immense period of time invertebrate life must have become very diverse and adapted to many varied habitats of the sea. By the end of the period weathering and erosion had reduced the level of the land and the supply of sandy material to the shallow seas diminished. The distinct difference between the fossil fauna of the Cambrian and Ordovician periods is, in part, a reflection of a time when a lower sea level exposed the low land and nondeposition was prevalent over broad areas.

When, at the beginning of the Ordovician, the seas again began to spread across the exposed land, the deposition of limestones became more

ERAS	PERIODS	EPOCHS	MILLIONS OF YEARS AGO	GENERALIZED BIOLOGICAL CONTINUUM	GENERALIZED GEOLOGIC EVENTS IN NORTH AMERICA
Cenozoic	Quaternary	Recent		Paleo-Indians Migrating to North America	Latest ice age begins
	Quaternary	Pleistocene	2		
	Tertiary	Pliocene		Man as a tool user	
	Tertiary	Miocene	25	First manlike primates	Continental seas less common than before, confined to basins for awhile
	Tertiary	Oligocene			
	Tertiary	Eocene			
	Tertiary	Paleocene		Placental mammals common	
Mesozoic	Cretaceous		65	Major extinctions (dinosaurs, etc.)	Folding and major uplifting of Rocky Mountain ranges
	Jurassic		135	First flowering plants; First birds	
	Triassic		190	First mammals; First dinosaurs; first mammal-like reptiles	
Paleozoic	Permian		225	Major extinctions (trilobites, etc.)	Folding and major uplifting of Appalachian Mountains
	Pennsylvanian		230	First reptiles	Potential coal forests in marshes of Eastern and Central U.S.
	Mississippian		325	First reptile-like amphibians	
	Devonian		350	First land animals (amphibians); First amphibian-like fish; First rooted land plants	Acadian Mountains of New England-Canada rising
	Silurian		400	First vertebrates (fish); Nearly all major invertebrate types present	Taconic Mountains of New York-Quebec rising
	Ordovician		430		
	Cambrian		500	Invertebrates common as fossils	
			600		
Precambrian				Cellular remains over 3 billion years old	Several major mountain ranges uplifted and eroded
			4600	Age of Earth	

Figure 8-1

PHYLUM	BIOLOGIC-FOSSIL CHARACTERISTICS	FIRST APPEARANCE	EXAMPLES
Protozoa	Microscopic, one celled animals with shells of calcium carbonate or silica.	Precambrian	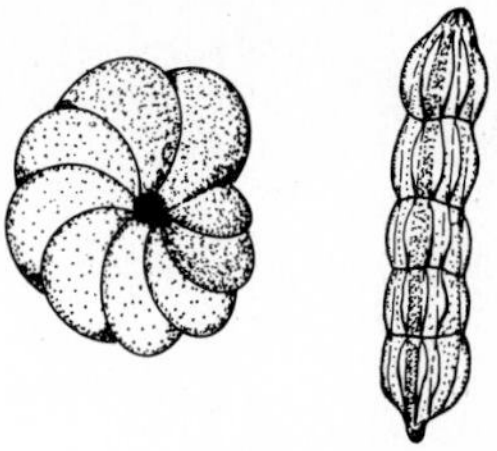
Porifera	Sponges with internal skeletal elements of calcium carbonate or silica.	Precambrian	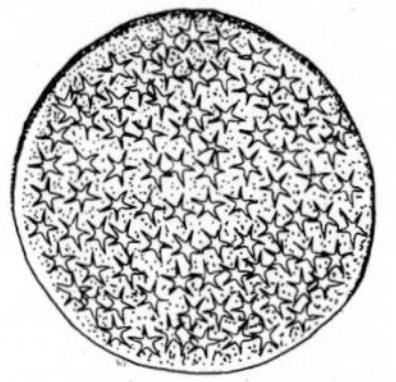
Coelenterata	Corals with shells of calcium carbonate. Solitary or colonial.	Ordovician	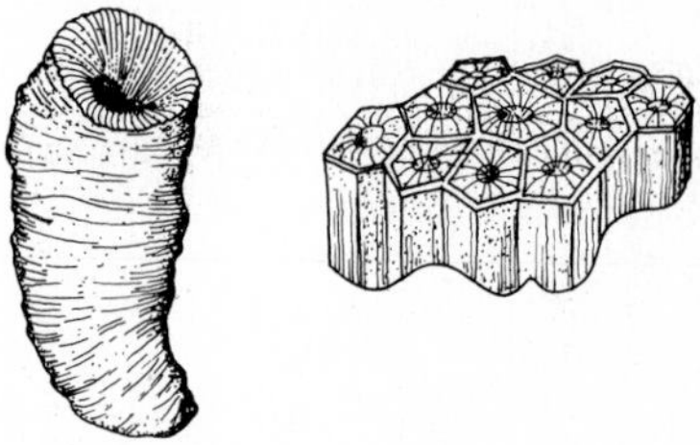
Bryozoa	Small colonial organisms in a larger calcium carbonate dwelling.	Cambrian	
Brachiopoda	Bivalved; the calcium carbonate valves of dissimilar shape.	Cambrian	 Side view Front view

Figure 8-2 Chart of the most commonly fossilized groups of invertebrate animals. The time of first appearance is a generally accepted one; specimens questionably belonging to the phylum may have been found in older strata. Some groups within a

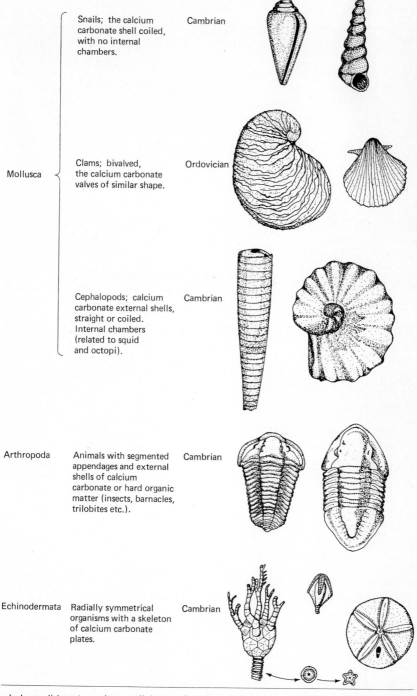

Mollusca	Snails; the calcium carbonate shell coiled, with no internal chambers.	Cambrian	
	Clams; bivalved, the calcium carbonate valves of similar shape.	Ordovician	
	Cephalopods; calcium carbonate external shells, straight or coiled. Internal chambers (related to squid and octopi).	Cambrian	
Arthropoda	Animals with segmented appendages and external shells of calcium carbonate or hard organic matter (insects, barnacles, trilobites etc.).	Cambrian	
Echinodermata	Radially symmetrical organisms with a skeleton of calcium carbonate plates.	Cambrian	

phylum did not evolve until long after the first known members of that phylum appeared. Other phyla well known today, such as worms, have left meager fossil records. All the listed phyla have living members.

(a)

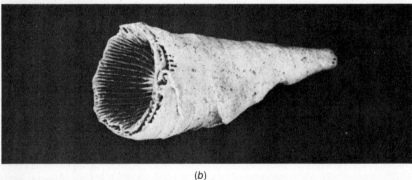

(b)

Figure 8-3 Typical Paleozoic marine invertebrate fossils from the central United States. (a) A colonial coral; (b) a solitary "horn" coral; (c) (opposite page) a trilobite; (d) (opposite page) a brachiopod.

common than the sandstones so prevalent in the Cambrian seas. The lack of highlands for a source of abundant particulate matter resulted in clear-water seas, but the extensive lime deposits also may be related to biochemical changes. The ability to extract calcium from seawater and to secrete calcium carbonate as shell material became widespread in the invertebrate realm. Clams, snails, corals, brachiopods, cephalopods (the shelled ancestors of today's octopus and squid), and many other forerunners of modern marine life thrived in the warm shallow seas (Figure 8-3). The Ordovician was a major period in the development of marine life, and by its end all the major marine invertebrate phyla were present. The trilobites entered the period with difficulty, for many of the Cambrian types had become extinct. Nonetheless,

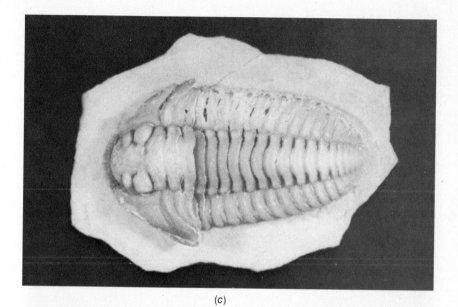

(c)

(d)

Figure 8-3 continued

the survivors came to flourish during Ordovician time and only afterward
began a general decline toward extinction.

The First Vertebrates   In the midst of all this invertebrate development, a
still somewhat mysterious event occurred. A few scraps of bones and
external armor plates have been found in Ordovician sandstone and,
recently, in limestone. These remains are of the earliest *vertebrate* organisms
yet discovered. By comparison with similar armor plates from better-
preserved material later in the Paleozoic, there is little doubt that small
armored jawless fish lived over 450 million years ago (Figure 8-4). The

Figure 8-4 This model is of one of the jawless armored fish that represent the first known vertebrate animals. The fish was flattened and its eyes were on the top of its head, so it probably lived on the bottom. *(Courtesy of American Museum of Natural History.)*

mystery is that no definite invertebrate candidates for the ancestors of these fish have been found. In all likelihood the vertebrate scheme, with a dorsal rather than ventral nerve cord and a somewhat unified internal skeletal support, arose before the Ordovician. What these fossil finds mark is the

Figure 8-5 *A Devonian forest.* This is an artist's idea of what a forest in eastern North America looked like some 360 million years ago. The fern tree on the right was over 10 meters high. *(Courtesy of Field Museum of Natural History.)*

hardening of these internal supports by the addition of calcium compounds. Most modern vertebrates have a bony spinal column which acts not only as support but also protects the dorsal nerve cord. However, some modern animals, sharks for example, have cartilage rather than bone supports. It is not unreasonable to suppose that vertebrates were present in pre-Ordovician time, but their supporting connective tissue was cartilaginous, not hardened or replaced by bone. These small earliest fish lacked jaws and, consequently, are known as *agnaths*. The sole survivors of the type today are the lamprey and hagfish. They do not seem to have been good swimmers since they lacked paired fins, but they were fairly streamlined. They may have inhabited rivers, a nice place for a poor swimmer since food may be brought to the fish by the running water. Marine fossils have been found in association with these fish fossils, but the latter could have been washed to the sea after death. The problem of where the earliest vertebrates lived and developed is unsolved.

By the Devonian period all the major groups of fish had evolved. Jaws and teeth (derived from scales) were characteristics quickly selected for, since they are a distinct food-gathering advantage. The armor of the early fish was lost, and the jawed fish evolved into the two lines now present: the bony fish (for example, today's trout and salmon) and the cartilaginous fish (sharks and rays). Fish with jaws may have played a role in the further decline of the trilobites, for only one major morphological group survived the period. The Devonian is called the Age of Fishes.

Paleozoic Plants   We haven't said much about plants, mostly because nothing much is known about any that inhabited the land in lower Paleozoic time. As far as we know, the landscapes were stark and barren for most of the earth's history. The first indication of land plants is in upper Silurian rocks. These primitive, woody-stemmed plants had no true roots or leaves and probably grew in ponds (Figure 8-5). Today there are a few very similar types still living. By the end of the Paleozoic, plants evolved to occupy much of the land. The extensive Pennsylvanian coal beds in North America are testimony to their abundance (Figures 8-6 and 8-7). Only one major botanical development was yet to come, the flowering plants.

The First Land Dwellers   Again, in the midst of success by one group of organisms, a major new group made its appearance. This seems to have been the case with all major changes in the evolution of animals. New forms which initiate a major change in life style or bodily functions seem to appear, not during a decline of their previously successful forebearers, but at the time of their dominance. As the fish evolved, two types of fin styles came into being (Figure 8-8). One, the *ray-finned* fish, had fins similar to nearly all the bony fish we know of today. Another group, the *lobe-finned* fish, had bony extensions into the fins, which were articulated with the internal skeleton. Both groups developed air sacs, probably for breathing air directly. In the

Figure 8-6   This scene depicts some of the plants and animals which existed during the Pennsylvanian and Permian periods. Note the large dragonfly at the lower right. Both roaches and dragonflies are known from rocks of the Pennsylvanian period and the living ones are among the few insects that retained their very ancient forms. The depicted one was, however, closer in size to a modern hawk.

    The Permian reptiles with the large dorsal "sail" may have used this large surface area of skin to help regulate their body temperature by either radiating or absorbing heat. From this stock were to come the mammallike reptiles and eventually the mammals. Perhaps these primitive thermoregulatory adaptations were advents of the warm blooded condition. *(Courtesy of the Peabody Museum of National History, Yale University.)*

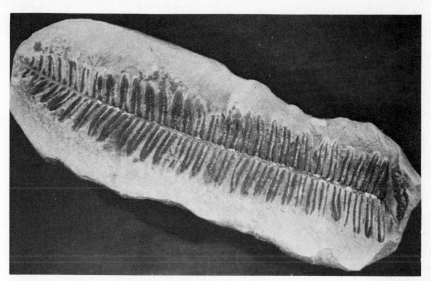

Figure 8-7 A Pennsylvanian plant fossil from Illinois.

modern ray-finned group this air sac now serves principally as a buoyancy mechanism and is commonly called a *swin bladder*. In the lobe-finned group this primitive lung seems to have been maintained and developed. Today, three species of lungfish exist; all can survive out of water and are capable of moving around on land. One deep-sea lobe-finned fish, the *coelocanth*, is more directly related to the early lobed-finned ones. Its type was considered long extinct until 1938, when one was caught off East Africa (Figure 8-8). Since then, many specimens have been found.

The capability of breathing air directly from the atmosphere and of moving across dry land on bony muscular extensions of the body opened new ways of life to Devonian vertebrates. Some of the fish, probably freshwater dwellers, as are modern lungfish, finally came to spend most of their lives out of water. Whether this was in response to a drying up of Devonian lakes, or whether they simply found food more abundant and with less competition on land, is debatable. At any rate, the transition to life on land had come for the vertebrates. The bony fins came to be what we call legs. Other skeletal and bodily changes occurred, but basically some fish had evolved in form and function to where the term fish became quite inappropriate. *Amphibians* were now colonizing the land (Figure 8-9).

The amphibians, today represented mostly by frogs, toads, newts, and salamanders, are still not completely at home on dry land. They still return to their ancestral home, the water, to lay their eggs. Their larval forms (tadpoles, for example) still breathe water and they usually have no scales. Their ancestors found many problems in living on land. Two major problems, the lack of buoyant support by water and the increased problems of temperature changes or of drying out, were finally overcome, but not quickly. From fish to amphibian required millions of years, and undoubtedly many types perished during the transformation.

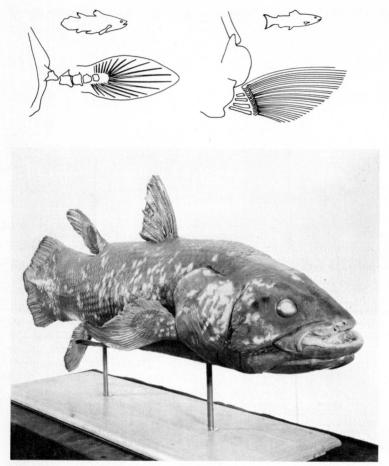

Figure 8-8   The drawing shows the arrangements of fin supports in typical lobe-finned (left) and ray-finned (right) fishes. In the lobe fins, muscles and bones extended into the fin, permitting greater control and flexibility of movement. Such fins developed into the limbs of the land-walking amphibians. The photograph shows a model of a modern lobe-finned fish. Until a fish like this was caught off East Africa, this type of lobe-finned fish was thought to have become extinct over 60 million years ago! *(Courtesy of American Museum of Natural History.)*

Reptiles—The Commitment to Land   In the Pennsylvanian period, on a land forested by large trees (over three-quarters of the world's coal is of this age) and in a moist, warm environment, life on land became abundant. Much of the land area of earth seems to have been warm, and coral reefs grew on what now is the island of Spitsbergen (latitude 78°N); Europe and North America may have been far south of their present positions. Insects crawled and flew and the ancestors of modern cockroaches and centipedes attained sizes, up to a foot long, that would surely startle a modern householder. Dragonflies had wing spans of over 2 feet. If the insects were ever to take over the earth, that was their chance. Amphibians, still with the bony skull armor their lobe-finned relatives had, were very common. Although most were small, some probably weighed several hundred pounds. From strata deposited on land during Pennsylvanian time came evidence of a new vertebrate group, the reptiles.

Reptiles most significantly differ from amphibians in the nature of their reproduction. Since that is not a phenomenon apt to be abundantly clarified by fossil remains, other characteristics must be examined. The skeletal elements of reptilian heads and the modifications of limb bones to turn the foot and knee forward and draw the limb farther beneath the body are some criteria that enable the paleontologist to tell the two apart. No well-preserved forms completely intermediate between amphibians and the earliest-known reptiles have been found. Reptiles probably evolved from fairly early amphibians, because some forms which have characteristics of both were living when reptiles were fairly well developed and diverse.

The most significant aspect of reptiles that enabled them to so rapidly gain superiority over the amphibians was their eggs. The amphibians had laid their unfertilized eggs like caviar to the hungry, in the water, and had to lay many for the few to survive. When the reptiles achieved internal fertilization, this allowed time for the egg to develop within the female and to permit secretion of a shell. The egg, when laid, was a protected self-contained home for the embryo, filled with nourishment and capable of gas exchange with the atmosphere. Open water was no longer a requisite for maintenance of the species. This advance was to make the next era, the Mesozoic, the Age of Reptiles. The amphibians have maintained a low profile ever since.

Extinctions   During or at the close of the Permian period, about 50 percent

Figure 8-9   Note the similarity between the lower drawing of a lobe-finned fish of 350 million years ago and the primitive amphibian that developed from fish of this type. *(Courtesy of American Museum of Natural History.)*

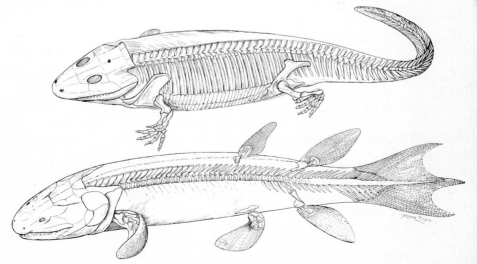

of all the known families of animals disappeared, worldwide. So many organisms became extinct that the major boundary between Paleozoic and Mesozoic came to be drawn. Widespread and abundant groups of organisms from diverse ways of life were unable to survive the transition from Permian to Triassic time. The trilobites had been declining for some time, but the reasons for the total disappearance of apparently successful groups of plants, corals, brachiopods, and many other types are unknown. No single catastrophic event occurred, but during the millions of years of transition from the one era to the next it is surprising that so many groups lacked the genetic variability necessary for survival.

The vast majority of fossil faunas are those of organisms that dwelt in shallow seas, and the breakup of the large supercontinent beginning about 225 million years ago, had a great effect on environment (Figure 8-10). The seas were withdrawing from the continents, and the formerly widespread shallow habitats became restricted to narrow newly created coastal zones. Biological competition, rates of natural selection and evolution, and extinctions increased. The changing climate, as new mountain chains and the different relationships between land and sea altered wind and oceanic current patterns, contributed to the changes. Many groups could not adapt and disappeared, while others barely survived into the Mesozoic; new forms evolved to fill the vacated habitats. Marine strata recording the time of era transition are not common, and part of our lack of knowledge is the result of the lack of preserved organisms. Yet the old question of why such a profound change in life forms occurred at this time in history cannot be dismissed by an insufficient rock record. The changes in life are probably testimony that the activity in the earth's interior which causes changes in sea-floor spreading and plate movements initiates biologic changes as well.

North America in the Paleozoic The changing levels of the seas during the 375 million years of Paleozoic time caused periodic retreats and advances across the North American continent. The sedimentary deposits in the central portion of the continent are comparatively thin, but along the ancient margins of the continent, great thicknesses of sediments were laid down. Upper Precambrian and Lower Cambrian sediments alone accumulated to thicknesses of thousands of meters in coastal belts, or geosynclines, a few hundred kilometers in length. These elongate geosynclinal zones were not great deep, empty troughs which began to receive the erosional debris of newly exposed land. These areas, zones of weakness along the continental and oceanic crustal margins, sank as they received the sediments and much of the rock is of shallow-water origin. As the sediments accumulated, their great mass began to initiate uplift as the isostatic balancing forces described in Chapter 3 came into play. Sea-floor spreading caused the subduction of oceanic plates along the ancient continental margins, or brought other ancient continents into collision with North America. These lateral forces folded, compressed, and faulted the sedimentary rocks, and volcanism and emplacement of granitic batholiths occurred. The history of major Paleozoic mountain building in North America is complex, and much is yet to be worked out.

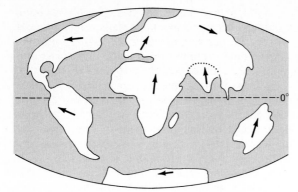

Today: arrows show relative movement directions

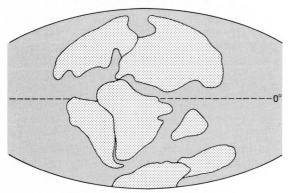

Jurassic-Cretaceous time: 135 million years ago

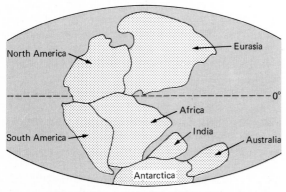

North America

Eurasia

Africa

India

South America

Australia

Antarctica

Permian-Triassic time: 225 million years ago

Figure 8-10 Generalized possible continental relationships since the end of the Paleozoic era.

The Atlantic coast, in the present area of New England and the Canadian maritime provinces, was the site of the first major Paleozoic mountain building. This region began to experience unrest during the Ordovician period. Geosynclinal sediments were uplifted and thrust northward and westward for many kilometers against the Canadian Shield. A mountain system about 3000 kilometers long, perhaps as high as the present Rockies, came into being. This event has been named the *Taconic* after the Taconic Mountains in New York. The Adirondacks, the Green Mountains, the lavas and intrusives of Newfoundland and the Gaspé are some of the products of these events. As soon as uplift occurred, weathering and erosion began, and now only a small remnant of this once-great range remains.

As erosion progressed in this region, seas once more transgressed over large areas. Volcanism was rampant and thousands of feet of ash and lavas of Silurian age were laid down in the seas. The Taconics shed their material and contributed sands and shales westward onto the continent and eastward into the seas. The thick limestones of the spectacular Gaspé coast are one example of shallow-water sediments laid down along the Devonian coastline. In this period, the second phase of mountain building, the *Acadian* began. Forces similar in direction to those of the Taconic event, but even more intense, folded and commonly metamorphosed rocks of the region and uplifted lofty mountains. Many intrusions not only gave rise to the granitic and metamorphic terrain of the Green Mountains of Vermont, but also are associated with valuable ore deposits of eastern Canada.

The mountain-building climax along the eastern margin of the United States came toward the end of the Paleozoic. Throughout hundreds of millions of years as much as 15,000 meters of sediment had accumulated along the sea-floor–continental margin. The early Atlantic Ocean is thought to have been closing during the Paleozoic. Both the Taconic and Acadian events may have been responses to forces initiated by subducting plates of Atlantic oceanic crust. But the latter event may mark the first slow but forceful collisions of North Africa and Europe with North America. Portions of these continents apparently collided to compress geosynclinal deposits and elevate them into mountain ranges here and in Britain, Greenland, and Scandinavia. Finally, in the late Paleozoic, the grand culmination of mountain building in eastern North America, the *Appalachian* event, began (Figure 8-11). From Newfoundland to Mexico the thick shallow-water miogeosynclinal and the deeper-water, thicker eugeosynclinal deposits farther offshore became part of North America. The deeper-water deposits had perhaps received some of their mass from adjacent North Africa and Europe. Thus, in the Permian, the compressive forces of continental collision, accompanied by volcanism and intrusion, uplifted a great range of mountains. The Appalachian geosyncline, in existence from late Precambrian time until late Paleozoic time, ceased to be. As the Paleozoic ended, some 225 million years ago, the joined continents severed again and the modern Atlantic Ocean was born.

What was happening in western North America while the eastern geosyncline was pulsating with Taconic, Acadian, and Appalachian mountain building? Most of this time the western third of the continent was the site of deposition of thick sediments in another geosyncline. Crustal unrest during

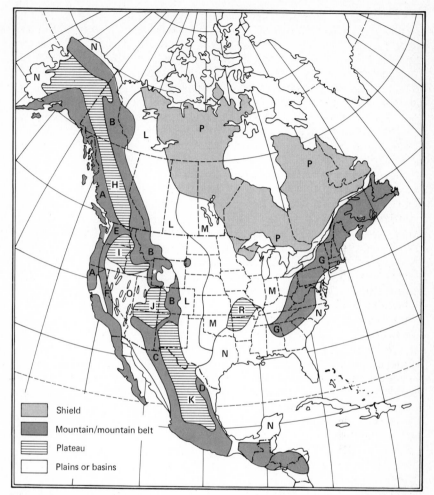

Figure 8-11 Principal physiographic regions of North America. (Compare with Figure 8-26.) A, coast ranges; B, Rocky Mountains; C, Western Sierra Madre; D, Eastern Sierra Madre; E, Cascade Range; F, Sierra Nevada; G, Appalachian Belt (including Plateau, Valley and Ridge, Blue Ridge, Piedmont, Adirondack, and various mountains of New England–Canadian Maritime regions); H, Canadian and Alaskan Plateau; I, Columbia Plateau (lavas); J, Colorado Plateau; K, Mexican Plateau; L, Great Plains; M, Interior Lowlands; N, Coastal Plain; O, Basin and Range (Sonora Desert to south); P, Canadian Shield; R, Interior Highlands (Ozarks and Ouachitas).

Mississippian time uplifted a long, narrow range from Arizona through Idaho and into Canada. As soon as this landmass rose, weathering and erosion began. We know of its existence by the thick deposits of gravel and sand washed from it into the seas to its west and east (Figure 8-12).

The Mississippian was the last time really widespread continental seas

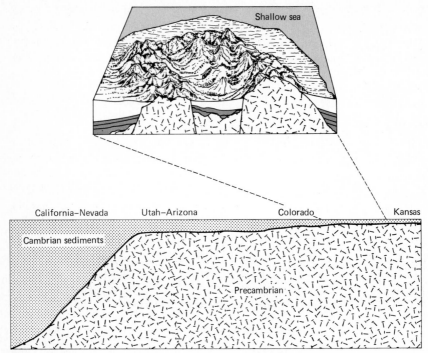

Figure 8-12 The lower diagram in an idealized restored cross section at the end of Cambrian time. The Precambrian continental mass has been overlain with marine Cambrian sediments. Similar-shaped sections could be drawn across the United States further north, or across western Canada. The deeper waters off the continental shelf, which ended in what is now Nevada, received up to 5000 meters of sediment along the subsiding continental margin. Sediments thinned eastward and only some 500 meters of Cambrian rocks are found in Arizona. Some areas to the east, in Canada especially, have no record of Cambrian seas and apparently had extensive lowlands exposed. The upper diagram shows the basic structure of an area of Colorado over 200 million years later in Pennsylvanian time, after additional sedimentation and after the Colorado Mountains had risen.

covered central North America. The western ranges which had risen during this period began to divide the zone of marine deposition into two parts, a Pacific geosyncline along what are now the West Coast states and another one essentially along the zone of the present Rocky Mountains (Figure 8-13). More on this later.

Activity increased during Pennsylvanian time and produced more land in the west. Ranges still visible in Texas, Arkansas, and Oklahoma were uplifted and a prominent chain of mountains developed across Colorado and parts of adjacent states. These Colorado Mountains, sometimes called the Ancestral Rockies, were the source of stream deposits which today form the famous "red rocks" of the Garden of the Gods and Redrock Park along the Colorado Front Range of the modern Rockies (Figure 8-12).

While the northern landmasses were apparently warm although somewhat arid during Permian time, the southern landmasses stood in stark contrast. Continental glaciation was occurring on what are now widely separated landmasses. Antarctica, India, South Africa, and South America were apparently joined or in close proximity, and their glacial deposits and similar floras provided some of the best evidence for early ideas on continental drift (Figure 3-26).

THE MESOZOIC ERA (225 TO 65 MILLION YEARS AGO)
For much of the Triassic period the continents remained emergent, and only toward the end did the seas transgress extensively. By this time, tens of

Figure 8-13 The geography of North American about 330 million years ago showing the shallow, widespread Mississippian continental sea.

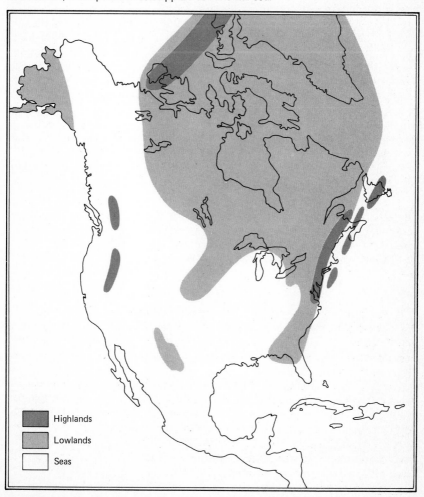

Highlands

Lowlands

Seas

millions of years into the period, life had become about as varied as it had been in the upper Paleozoic. Among the multitudes of invertebrate life in the Mesozoic seas, the molluscs became predominant. Ammonites flourished, oysters first appeared, clams diversified and proved more efficient users of the habitats brachiopods had enjoyed, and the latter group was never to become prolific again (Figure 8-14).

On land, ferns and conifers were common in the Triassic forests, and hints of the first flowering plants have been found. In the Cretaceous period the flowering plants flourished and fossil pollen and leaves indicate that a modern-type flora existed before the era closed. The changing composition of plant populations was matched by the changes in terrestrial life.

The Reptile Dynasty Some Permian vertebrate groups survived into the early Mesozoic, but most of these became extinct. The amphibians were reduced to the relatively insignificant status they now have, and the first frogs and salamanders evolved during the era.

From their late Paleozoic beginnings, the reptiles evolved rapidly and came to occupy diverse environments on land, in the seas, and in the air. In Triassic strata, evidence has been found that one group of small, apparently carnivorous vertebrates was widespread and of a significantly different lineage from most reptiles. Their teeth, in contrast to those of a typical reptile, which tend to be all of similar shape, were differentiated. This, and more subtle skeletal evidence, indicates that mammal-like reptiles had evolved in the Permian and were successful during the Triassic period. True mammals were yet to evolve and their time of dominance was yet to come. But they were developing during the millions of years of reptilian rule.

In the Triassic, two large groups of reptiles developed. These two groups, not directly related, are differentiated by the skeletal form of their pelvic

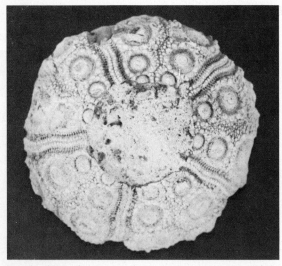

(a)

Figure 8-14 Mesozoic marine invertebrate fossils. (a) A sea urchin from England; (b) (opposite page) a clam from North Dakota; (c) (opposite page) a coral from Montana.

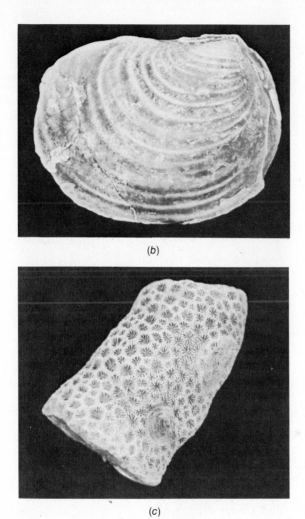

(b)

(c)

Figure 8-14 continued

bones. Because some members of each of these two groups attained enormous sizes, they became famous as the *dinosaurs*. The word, derived from Greek, means "terrible lizards," and although some would qualify as such, others were the size of chickens and many were placid eaters of plants. One bipedal group evolved into the largest carnivorous land animals of all time, such as *Tyrannosaurus* (Figure 8-15) in the Cretaceous. Probably standing over 6 meters and with long, pointed conical reptilian teeth, they were formidable creatures. Another group, with the same basic pelvic structure, evolved into the quadrupedal plant-eating giants which were the largest terrestrial animals of any type ever known; some weighed over 50 tons and others were nearly 30 meters in length (Figure 8-16). Possibly to help support their weight, these large reptiles may have spent much of their

Figure 8-15 Over 70 million years ago, in Late Cretaceous time, dinosaurs like these walked the plains of western North America. The largest meat-eater known, *Tyrannosaurus* stood about 6 meters high. Flowering plants, which first appeared in Mesozoic time, are also shown. *(Courtesy of Peabody Museum of Natural History.)*

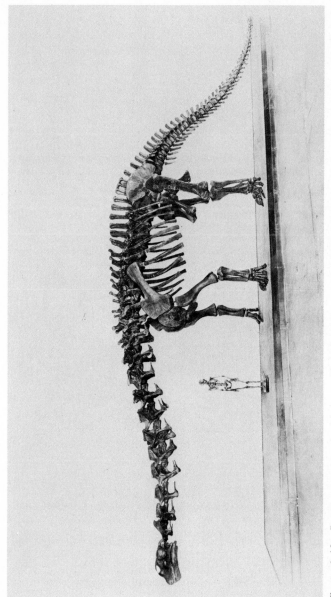

Figure 8-16 *Brontosaurus, an herbivorous Jurassic dinosaur. (Courtesy of American Museum of Natural History.)*

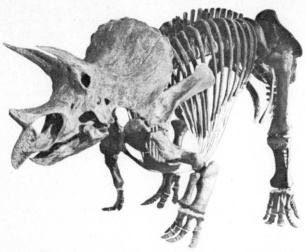

Figure 8-17 *Triceratops*, a common, very large, Cretaceous herbivorous dinosaur of the "bird-hip" type that lived in western North America. *(Courtesy of Minnesota Science Museum.)*

Figure 8-18 Animals like these Mesozoic reptiles were very common in the shallow seas that covered large areas of North America during the Mesozoic era. Most swimming reptiles became extinct at the end of that era. Their places in the environment were taken by whales, porpoises, and other mammals. *(Courtesy of Field Museum of Natural History.)*

time in the swampy environments near lakes and rivers, where their food was abundant.

The other type of pelvic structure common to some dinosaur groups is more birdlike rather than typically reptilian. *Birdlike* is a term applied in retrospect, since birds evolved after that type of hip-girdle first appeared. Delicacy is not implied in the term, for some ponderous beasts had birdlike pelves (Figure 8-17). All these bird-hip types, bipedal and quadrupedal, are thought to have been herbivorous.

During the Mesozoic some groups of reptiles went back to their ancestral home, the sea (Figure 8-18). Commonly streamlined and with their limbs transformed to paddle-shaped fins, they became the Mesozoic counterparts of some modern mammals, the whales and porpoises for example, which also reverted to aquatic life.

Of obvious reptilian stock, but with unknown direct ancestors, two groups of flying reptiles appeared in the Jurassic. These interesting creatures possibly evolved from small tree dwellers that developed the ability to glide from tree to tree. They developed light hollow bones and a keel on the breastbone for the attachment of powerful wing muscles. One of their "fingers" became elongate, and a thin skin stretched from there to the body (Figure 8-19). Early ones maintained a primitive tail, and some had teeth while others lost them in favor of a horny beak. At the end of Cretaceous time, some had a wingspread of 15 meters (50 feet)!

How these flying reptiles took off with their enormous wingspan is

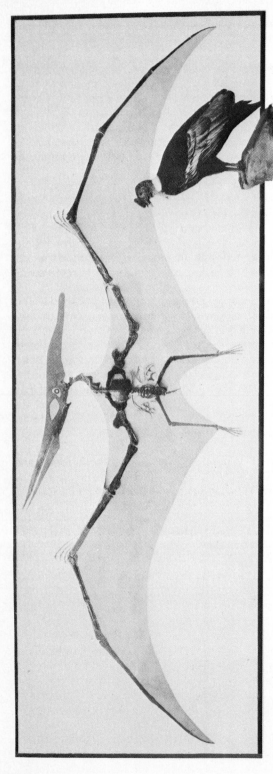

Figure 8-19 Nearly 100 million years ago this reptile was flying over what is now Kansas. When it died, its skeleton was preserved in the chalky muds of a shallow continental sea. A mounted specimen of one of the largest living birds, the condor, is beside it. *(Courtesy of American Museum of Natural History.)*

questionable. Some were probably reasonably efficient flappers, but the larger ones probably glided and soared. The necessity for high-energy expenditures to begin and maintain flight, especially in cool weather, may indicate they had a metabolic system more like modern birds than modern reptiles.

Today nearly all reptiles are represented by a few thousand species of crocodile types, lizards, turtles, and snakes. All these appeared during the Mesozoic era; the snakes, with only internal vestiges of their legs, were the last reptiles to come onto the scene. All modern reptiles are "cold"-blooded, their internal body temperature tending to be the same as that of their surroundings. When the weather is cold, reptiles become sluggish since their body temperatures and metabolic activity are low. They can elevate their temperature by absorbing external heat, and may spend their active periods with their "cold" blood warmer than that of most "warm"-blooded organisms. A snake, for example, crawls onto a warm rock and basks in the sun to warm up and permit increased activity.

If the diverse types of large Mesozoic reptiles were all cold-blooded, it is difficult to explain how they became so widely spread. During most of the Mesozoic era, the climate seems to have been warmer and without the distinct latitudinal climatic zones we have now. Yet there is reason to suppose that they successfully invaded cooler temperate zones. Small reptiles can survive cold weather in burrows, as snakes and lizards of the northern United States and Canada do now, but large ones cannot—if they are cold-blooded. Some dinosaur groups and other Mesozoic reptiles may have been warm-blooded, at least to some degree. Analysis of the internal structure of their bones indicates this is a likely possibility.

Birds Birds and mammals are the only warm-blooded animals today, and both evolved from reptilian stock. Feathers were derived from scales, and the earliest known bird fossils, from the Jurassic, show impressions of feathers (Figure 8-20). Yet these birds are nothing more than feathered reptiles and show little of the skeletal changes common to birds today. By Cretaceous time the long reptilian tail had disappeared and the bones were hollow, but they still seem to have had teeth.

Mammals From their origin as mammallike reptiles in late Paleozoic time, the first true mammals appeared in the Triassic period. The biological characteristics of mammals most commonly used to define them—a warm-blooded metabolism, the presence of hair, and the provision of milk for the newborn—are difficult to tell from fossil remains. Fortunately, skeletal differences also occur; for example, a reduction of the number of bones in the skull and lower jaw, different ear bones, and the differentiation of teeth shapes. These and other characteristics, taken together, tell the story of the early mammals. While small, but with larger brains compared to reptiles of similar size, they were successful in the midst of the reptilian heyday and radiated to all continents. By the end of Cretaceous time the three main subclasses of mammals had evolved: the egg layers such as today's duck-billed platypus, the pouched marsupials such as today's kangaroo and

(a)

Figure 8-20 The fossil skeleton of the earliest bird known, about 150 million years old (Jurassic), is shown on the left. The impression left by the feathers can be seen clearly. In the reconstruction on the right the claws along the edge of the wings and the teeth are visible. Without the feather impressions as a clue, the skeleton might have been classed as a reptile. *(Courtesy of American Museum of Natural History and Peabody Museum of Natural History, Yale University.)*

opossum, and the most common placentals with young developed totally within the mother before live birth.

Extinctions The long reptilian play closed at the end of the Mesozoic era. A great organic event occurred, geologically rather suddenly, and gave cause for geologists to name a new era. Not one dinosaur is known to have existed into the Cenozoic. Large mammals did not exist at the end of Cretaceous time, so direct competition was not the cause of the mass extinction. Life in the sea came to similar fates, but not only the large marine reptiles disappeared. Many previously abundant forms of invertebrates, swimmers (all the ammonites), bottom dwellers (many groups of clams), and floaters (many groups of planktonic microorganisms) suffered extinction.

(*b*)

Some groups in all habitats diminished in number toward the end of the Cretaceous, but others seem to have prospered until the end. What happened is unknown. Some event, or more probably events, of planetary scale must have changed the environment too rapidly for the populations of many organisms to evolutionarily adapt. Speculation concerning what these changes were range from a combination of minor things to excessive radiation from a supernova. Uncomfortable with unknown cataclysmic causes, most geologists have tried to explain the great demise by speculating on sea-level changes, the supply of nutrients to the seas, the rise of the flowering plants, climatic change, and variations in the composition of the atmosphere. These are only a few of the proposed causes, but all seem somewhat unsatisfactory, for it is difficult to show how they affected so many realms of life simultaneously.

North America in the Mesozoic With the seas mostly in the confines of the ocean basins, Triassic sediments are typically stream deposits. In the East the rapidly eroding Appalachians were the source of coarse debris that was deposited in large downfaulted basins. These feldspar-rich stream deposits were laid down close to their source, before much chemical weathering could occur. The small percentage of iron-bearing minerals rapidly oxidized to hematite and gave the sediments a red color. These oxidized "red beds" are typical of Triassic rocks on several continents and seem to be evidence of a generally warm climate, either arid or with seasonal rainfall. During the Mesozoic the Appalachians were not entirely quiescent, but upfaulted blocks were rapidly eroded. The range was reduced to a low plain, and Cretaceous seas transgressed over what is now the Atlantic coastal plain.

In the Gulf Coast area, earlier Jurassic seas had edged northward over the continent and during Cretaceous time advanced to what is now Illinois. The Mesozoic deposits are common reservoirs for the abundant petroleum of the Southern United States.

In western North America, the landmasses which had risen in late Paleozoic time continued to be active zones. Volcanism and intrusions in the Triassic produced islands and local volcanic ranges from Alaska all along western Canada. By Cretaceous time the extensive landmasses in the west had contributed tremendous quantities of sediment westward into the Pacific geosyncline and eastward into the Rocky Mountain geosyncline (Figure 8-21). It has been estimated that as much as 4 million cubic kilometers of sediment were deposited on each side! On the eastern side a broad system of river, floodplain, swamp, and lake deposits developed during the Triassic and Jurassic periods. The Jurassic Morrison Formation is an example, and from its beds have come some of the most significant dinosaur fossils ever found. Late in the Jurassic, seas from the north transgressed again over the area of the present Northern Rockies and from the south across Mexico and Texas.

The Cretaceous period was the time of the last major marine transgression onto North America. From the Rocky Mountain geosyncline the seas advanced until, about 100 million years ago, their shorelines were as far east as the site of Lake Superior (Figure 8-21). This Cretaceous transgression was worldwide.

In Jurassic and Cretaceous time, the Sierra Nevada and areas to the north were first uplifted and were the sites of volcanism and batholithic granitic intrusion. It is likely that these areas formed in response to subduction of an oceanic plate beneath the continental crust. Beginning in late Cretaceous time, and continuing with full strength into the Cenozoic era, the uplift of the Rocky Mountains occurred. Along a zone a few hundred kilometers wide and perhaps 18,000 kilometers long, deformed by eastward directed forces, the thick sediments were uplifted. The sediments of the Rocky Mountain geosyncline were not highly metamorphosed but were folded and formed a series of elongate upwarps cored by old Precambrian igneous and metamorphic rocks. As mentioned in Chapter 3, the relationship of plate tectonics to the Rockies is puzzling, for they certainly do not seem to be the result of continental collision or of typical subduction processes as are the Sierra Nevada and the still active Andes Mountains.

The large supercontinent, which began to break up at the end of

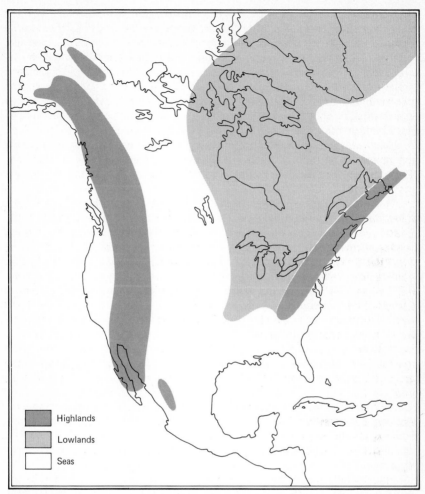

Figure 8-21 The geography of North America about 100 million years ago during Cretaceous time.

Paleozoic time, still retained some land connections during most of the Mesozoic era. Some of the more cosmopolitan types of dinosaurs, for example the long-necked herbivore *Brachiosaurus*, the largest land animal known to have existed, have been found in Jurassic rocks of central North America, East Africa, and Europe. Although continental masses such as Australia were severed and became relatively isolated, even as late as Late Cretaceous time the same types of dinosaurs lived in what is now Montana and Mongolia. Perhaps at the time the continental breakup was complete and these fossils represent only the isolated remnants of populations once widespread.

THE CENOZOIC ERA (65 MILLION YEARS AGO TO NOW)

The few groups of reptiles that survived into the Tertiary period, and survive today, were not much competition for the mammals. The latter, perhaps weighing less than half a kilogram to a few kilograms, quadrupedal with five toes, and having relatively small brain capacities compared to modern mammals, were left in dominance by default. Within a few million years the great mammalian expansion was underway, and with it commonly came an increase in size of both body and brain. Continental fragmentation resulted in the isolation of some groups; the pouched mammals were restricted to Australia and South America, where they then evolved independently. The egg layers, more reptilian than other mammals, were and are restricted to Australia, which was already well on its way northward toward its present position.

In the early Tertiary, some groups lost their side toes and the other toes developed into hoofs. Two main branches evolved, those with an even number of toes, to become today's cloven-hooved deer and cattle, and an odd-toed group. The latter group is represented now by such animals as the rhinoceros and, after complete reduction of all the toes but one, by the modern horse. Claws and horns evolved, dentition became even more varied, and by the late Tertiary the entire very diverse mammalian fauna had a distinctly modern aspect.

The tendency of some mammalian groups toward large size is exemplified by a hornless rhinoceros of the Oligocene epoch which stood about 5 meters high (Figure 8-22). Fossil bones and teeth are easier to find if their bearers were large, so we are a bit biased in our knowledge of Cenozoic mammals. Nevertheless, many types evolved to large size, more so than now exist; in the Pleistocene, animals closely related to modern ones were commonly much larger. Giant deer, dogs and buffalo, a beaver the size of a modern bear, and a pig as big as a modern rhino—all evolved, were widespread, but became extinct.

Were human beings the cause of the Pleistocene extinctions of these large mammals, or did some other factors place insurmountable pressures on their populations? People probably hunted some to extinction, and perhaps they fired the grasslands, but they cannot be held accountable for it all. Even with an abundance of fossils, we can only speculate.

Primates and the Human Family   In the early Tertiary period the first primates lived, probably descendants of small insect eaters present during the late Mesozoic. The primate condition of an opposable thumb for grasping, forward-directed eyes for overlapping stereovision and depth perception, and a large brain in relation to body size appeared well over 50 million years ago. These characteristics seem to have been evolutionarily selected for life in trees, where most primate species still live.

The most primitive primates are the *lemurs* (Figure 8-23), now found only on the island of Madagascar off East Africa. (All lemurs are on *The United States List of Endangered Fauna*.) A slightly more advanced group in the Tertiary was the *tarsiers*, and they are reduced now to one species in the East Indies and Philippines. Both these groups existed in North America, but

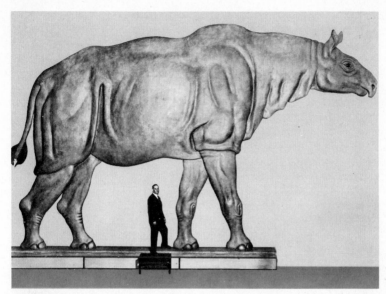

Figure 8-22 A reconstruction of a hornless rhinoceros, *Baluchitherium*, from the Oligocene epoch. It is the largest land mammal yet known to have existed. (The largest animal known, past or present, is the living mammal the blue whale.) *(Courtesy of American Museum of Natural History.)*

apparently the environment here became unfavorable approximately 35 million years ago; no primates are known to have been here from that time until quite recently when humans migrated in.

Modern Egypt can lay claim to traces not only of one of the oldest civilizations, but also of the oldest advanced primates. About 100 kilometers south of Cairo, in strata about 40 million years old, the earliest monkeys have been found. That these arboreal creatures lived in the area of the present Sahara desert is another reminder of the unstable nature of our planet. Today, there are two main groups of monkeys. Those of the Americas are somewhat more primitive and usually have tails with enough muscular control that they function almost as fifth limbs. Those of the Old World, principally in Asia and Africa, have slightly different dentition and tails useful only for balance. The two groups have been long separated and may have evolved from a common tarsierlike ancestor. If so, they are an excellent example of independent evolution along parallel lines. No evolutionary offshoots are known from the New World group, but this may be because South American fossil primate finds are rare.

The Old World monkeys early in their evolution toward their modern species are thought to have had a divergent group develop, which we see as being more apelike than monkey. From that time, on the basis of what we know from the very few good mid-Tertiary fossils, the higher primates evolved in Africa. Fossils from early Miocene strata in eastern Africa indicate that more than one apelike type was living about 25 million years ago. The

Figure 8-23 A drawing of a small modern lemur from Madagascar, an example of a primitive primate. Note digits which have developed for grasping and its intense power of concentration, typical of some higher primates.

evolutionary history of these groups is not known with any degree of certainty. Whether human beings and the modern group of apes were derived from the same primitive apelike forms or whether human beings were an evolutionary offshoot of the African apes at a later date is unknown. Blood-chemistry studies have indicated that the modern human is more closely related to the African apes, gorillas, and chimpanzees than to Asian ones such as orangutans, and so the second theory seems preferable for now.

In mid-Tertiary time, some of the tropical forests were being replaced by grasslands. Though most primates stayed with the retreating forests, at least one type was changing and adapting to life on the ground. Its hind legs lengthened and its feet flattened, making an upright stance and the ability to rise and search the horizon for food and enemies easier. The ability to occasionally stand and move rapidly on the hind limbs freed the forelimbs for uses other than moving through the trees. Already adapted for grasping, they could now be used more and more to pick berries or grab small insects or animals. In deposits in India and Africa, fossils of what most scientists consider the earliest member of the human family have been found. The

African fossils have been radiometrically dated at about 14 million years, upper Miocene. This genus, *Ramapithecus*, is classified principally on the basis of teeth and jaw fragments, but in contrast to typical apes, the snout is flattened, the canine teeth are much smaller, and the overall shape of the dental arch is more humanlike (Figure 8-24). *Ramapithecus* was small, probably weighed less than half as much as an average modern human, and had a brain case about one-fifth as big.

The scarcity of higher primate fossils from the time of *Ramapithecus* to about 2 million years ago makes it necessary to read between the lines of the evolutionary story of the human race. About 50 years ago in Africa, the first fossils of humanlike primates which seem to represent a definite transition from the apes were found. Since then hundreds of specimens of these have been found in Africa and Asia. Named *Australopithecus*, they seem to have consisted of at least two specific types; they had an erect stance and some used stone "tools." The diversity and variability of the australopithecines have caused problems in interpreting their history and relationships with more modern humans. They may have appeared as early as 5 or 6 million years ago, and relatively abundant remains of the type have been found in strata 2 million years old or less.

Whether some of the later australopithecine types belong to the genus of modern humans, *Homo*, or not is controversial. It must be remembered that what to name an organism is a decision of a modern person; nothing innate in nature demands it be given a particular name. How much variation from the skeletal nature of a modern human "norm" is permissible within the *idea* of

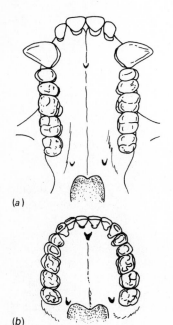

(a)

(b)

Figure 8-24 Dental arches of (*a*) a modern gorilla and (*b*) a modern man. Note the U-shaped arch and the large canine teeth of the gorilla and the more circular arch and much subdued canines in modern man.

the genus *Homo* is not within agreed-upon rigid confines. Since evolution is a continuum of change at variable rates and an individual fossil represents only a stage in the continuum, this is not surprising. A stage in the continuum that nearly all scientists agree was a member of our genus is represented by fossil teeth, skull, and limb bones from Asia, Africa, and Europe. First found in Java, *Homo erectus* had about twice the brain capacity of its australopithecine ancestors and half the capacity of our brain. A user of self-shaped tools

Figure 8-25 Replicas of fossil skulls of early hominids. (*a*) *Australopithecus africanus* skull and lower jaw showing U-shaped dental arch; (*b*) *Homo erectus*, skull and upper dentition showing more modern circular arch. *(Courtesy K. Moran.)*

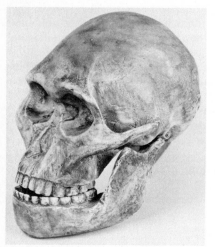
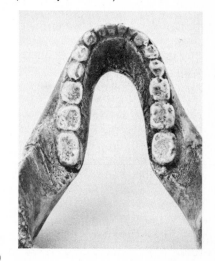

(a)

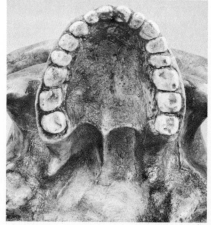

(b)

of stone, and in some regions fire, it apparently lived while some australopithecine types still existed. *Man*, as a *genus*, has probably inhabited earth for over 1 million years, and as a "human" for several million more (Figure 8-25).

North America in the Cenozoic   Along the eastern margin of North America, most of the once-high Appalachian chain had eroded to a low plain by early Cenozoic time. Only a few isolated peaks and low mountainous areas proved resistant. The White Mountains of New Hampshire and the Smoky Mountains of Tennessee–North Carolina are two of the larger areas apparently never reduced to a near-sea-level elevation. Beginning in mid-Cenozoic time vertical isostatic adjustments caused a rejuvenation of the range, uplifting the area about 1200 meters and exposing the nearly level erosional surfaces, now seen as the flattened summits of many Appalachian mountains. The new erosional base level caused rivers to cut and sculpture the surface, finally resulting in the present, but of course temporary, topography of the range (Figure 8-26).

The Appalachian Mountains are the result of surficial and deep-seated processes at work for over 500 million years. Most of the world's major mountain ranges have long histories of deposition, intercontinental action, uplift, erosion, and rejuvenation. These events are complex, not systematic or confined to small spans of time. The sediments eroded from the Appalachians and deposited in the sea along the eastern margin of North America are now kilometers thick. The material ingredients of future ranges are accumulating. To imagine that the uplift of the Appalachian Mountains at the close of the Paleozoic era ended the narrative is to make a short story out of a great continuing epic of nature.

The Cenozoic era was a time of abundant sedimentation along the Gulf Coast. Transgressions and regressions of the sea reworked the debris transported there from the continental interior and the Appalachian area. The area was not subject to mountain-building forces, and the Tertiary sediments are often loosely consolidated and dip gently seaward. Florida was a shallow bank accumulating limestone deposits, as it was during much of the

Figure 8-26 A generalized cross section of the United States indicating major physiographic and structural features. (Compare with Figure 8-11.)

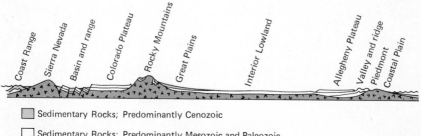

Coast Range Sierra Nevada Basin and range Colorado Plateau Rocky Mountains Great Plains Interior Lowland Allegheny Plateau Valley and ridge Piedmont Coastal Plain

☐ Sedimentary Rocks; Predominantly Cenozoic

☐ Sedimentary Rocks; Predominantly Mesozoic and Paleozoic

☐ Igneous and Metamorphic Rocks; Predominantly Precambrian

Mesozoic era. Off the continental margin, in the Gulf, the crust subsided under the great weight of accumulating sediment; a thickness of over 9000 meters is known to have accumulated during the Cenozoic. The crustal downwarping produced faults as the sediment was being deposited, and these often formed traps for accumulating petroleum. Some geologists consider the Gulf Coast a "modern" geosyncline, just as the Atlantic margin may be, and the site of eventual mountains. Time will tell.

In western North America, Rocky Mountain building largely ceased about 40 or 50 million years ago. The horizontal forces which produced much of the folding and early uplift gave way to the vertical movements of isostatic adjustments of the greatly thickened crust. Weathering and erosion eventually caused intermontane basins to fill and also produced the great wedge of stream deposits extending eastward into Kansas and Nebraska to form the Great Plains. Lakes developed in some of the basins, and in one of these, in the area of present Wyoming, the Green River Formation, famous as an oil shale and for its fish fossils (Figure 8-27), was deposited.

At about this time erosion had eliminated much of the former relief in the area and much of the Rockies probably stood only 600 to 900 meters in elevation. Vertical uplift of 1500 meters or more over a broad region induced new erosion and topographic relief. This uplift probably is still in progress. In general, the rising Rocky Mountains caused the continental interior of North America to become drier and cooler than before. One of the spectacular features of vertical uplift is the Colorado Plateau. During the compressive phase of the mountain building, its Paleozoic and Mesozoic rocks were somehow largely undeformed. Into these strata, rivers cut downward and in the late Cenozoic produced the Grand Canyon, which the Colorado River continues to modify today. Over 1600 meters deep, its walls rise to about 3000 meters above sea level.

Figure 8-27 Fish fossils in the Green River formation of Wyoming, of Eocene age.

Figure 8-28   Several small ranges of the Basin and Range province are visible. Great Salt Lake, a remnant of the much larger Lake Bonneville of Pleistocene time, is in the foreground.

Beginning in the Miocene epoch, a broad zone from Nevada into Mexico was affected by crustal movements which created an extensive system of northerly trending normal faults. A series of over 150 small isolated mountain ranges and basins were produced (the former once described as looking like "an army of caterpillars marching to Mexico"), to form the Basin and Range province (Figures 8-26 and 8-28).

The Sierra Nevada had its mountainous topography eroded away during Tertiary time. The present range is a redevelopment produced by a massive fault block developed late in the Cenozoic era. The eastern side is one of the steepest mountain flanks known and rises over 3000 meters above the bordering valley. Total displacement of the fault may exceed 6000 meters. Nearby, at about the same time, a downfaulted block produced the lowest area in North America, Death Valley.

Throughout much of Cenozoic time, volcanism was common in western North America. Volcanic ash contributed to deposits in the intermontane basins of the Rockies. In Washington, Oregon, and Idaho basaltic lava flowed from fissures to cover an area of some 500,000 square kilometers (Figure 3-7). The accumulations, which in some areas continued to recent times, are generally about 1500 meters thick.

In middle and late Cenozoic time the western margin of the Americas was often the site of intense volcanic activity. The Cascade Ranges from northern California into British Columbia are an example, and snow-capped volcanic peaks over 4000 meters high contribute to the beautiful scenery of the area (Figures 3-1 and 3-2). In the 48 states, Mount Lassen in California is the only known active volcano in the United States, but some of the others are probably just dormant. (Mount Baker in Washington has been showing signs of awakening.)

The Pacific margin of the Americas is still an active plate boundary. Volcanism continues in Alaska and from Mexico southward, and the intervening San Andreas fault system with its lateral motion (Figure 3-11) is a site of periodic earthquake activity. As America moved westward, the area of present California and northwest Mexico apparently overrode the spreading center called the East Pacific Rise. Much of the complex geology and Cenozoic igneous activity of the coastal area is related to this. The past and present relations between the western margin of the North American plate and the Pacific plate are not well understood. Controversy is very prevalent about the application of the modern theory of plate tectonics, not only to the present coastal areas, but also to the Rocky Mountains themselves, portions of which are 1600 kilometers inland.

The Pleistocene Ice Age   As mentioned in Chapter 4, continental glaciers covered much of North America until a few thousand years ago. Large-scale continental glaciation was not restricted to the Pleistocene Ice Age, which began over 2 million years ago. Yet the three most recent previous events, approximately 700, 400, and 270 million years ago, were widely separated in time. It would appear that some very unusual circumstances must be involved. No one has put forth to the satisfaction of a majority of scientists a total theory that explains why major ice ages begin and end. The idea of plate tectonics easily leads to the supposition that, occasionally, continents may be carried into polar latitudes and glaciation would thus occur. This does seem to be the major factor, but polar position is only part of the answer. For example, Antarctica is thought to have occupied a polar position long before glaciation started there some 10 million years ago. In addition to a polar location, a continent must receive snow and be at a sufficient elevation to prevent summer melt from removing all of it. Oceanic and atmospheric circulations are involved, and continental relationships even in equatorial regions affect both of these. Most scientists believe that some variation in the world's climate is necessary to initiate a major glacial period. These variations have been attributed to such things as less solar radiation or an increase in volcanic "dust" in the atmosphere, which inhibits the penetration of solar energy. Perhaps the approximate 300-million-year periodicity between some glaciations is tied to circumstances of a galactic nature. Our sun is thought to have rotated around the center of our galaxy about once every 400 million years in early Precambrian time and now, since it is apparently moving closer to the galactic center through time, about once each 275 million years.

The earth's climate seems to have been on a cooling trend during the Cenozoic era. Within this trend, evidence based primarily on fossil and oxygen isotope studies has indicated that many minor fluctuations in temperature have occurred. Climatic variation through time is becoming a more common field of research and, hopefully, perhaps the questions about continental glaciations can soon be answered.

Figure 8-29 illustrates the maximum extent in North America of the

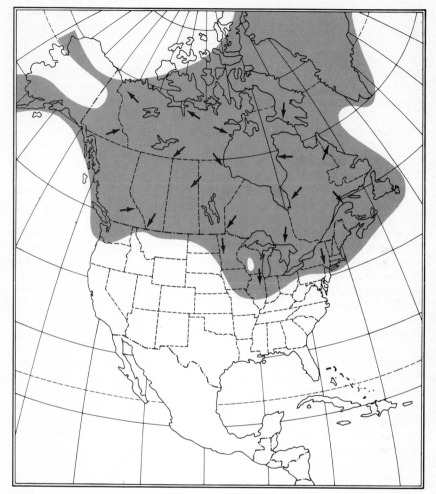

Figure 8-29 Maximum extent of the main Pleistocene ice sheets in North America. The arrows indicate flow directions.

Pleistocene ice sheets. These immense sheets of ice had strong effects on the climate of North America and directly or indirectly on its present topography. Cape Cod, for example, is a glacial moraine, and Bunker Hill is a hill of till. Northern Europe, southern South America, New Zealand, and areas of Asia were also ice-covered. In North America the ice had four major periods of advance. Within each period of advance, minor retreats and readvances occurred and the erosional and depositional legacies of each make glacial stratigraphy difficult. Figure 4-27 shows some of the long arcuate moraines left by the last ice sheet which retreated into Canada about 10,000 years ago.

The great weight and erosional effects of the ice, which was up to 3000 meters thick, smoothed and rounded the topography over which it advanced and gave the Great Lakes their present forms. Since so much water was in the frozen state, sea level was lowered approximately 130 meters below the present level. This worldwide change in base level caused increased stream erosion and the exposure of broad coastal areas which are now water-covered owing to the melting of the glaciers and hence higher sea level. Beach sands can be found on the bottom of the Atlantic many kilometers off the present shore.

The mass of ice, in some areas probably over 3000 meters thick and thus equivalent in weight to 1000 meters or more of rock, depressed the land. Since the last retreat, isostatic rebound has raised some parts of North America nearly 270 meters. This rebound is still occurring, and the region along the St. Lawrence River and the northern shores of the Great Lakes may be rising about 3 to 6 millimeters per year.

The Rocky Mountains in Canada were the site of large ice accumulations which occasionally merged with the continental ice sheets to the east. To the south the ice buildup was less, but the Rockies of the United States had extensive glaciation. These glaciers and the increased rainfall during the Pleistocene sculptured much of the beautiful scenery of today. The increased rainfall also led to the creation of abundant lakes in areas which are now much more arid. Great Salt Lake in Utah, now less than 10 meters deep, was over 300 meters deep and well over 10 times as large as now. The lake in its former state, known as Lake Bonneville, was fresh. The salts added to the lake waters by rain, saline springs, and streams which flowed over exposed marine strata later became concentrated by evaporation.

Since most of the fresh water on earth is in the frozen state, it is debatable whether or not we are still in a glacial age. During the interglacial periods of the Pleistocene, the ice may have retreated to the positions it now occupies. It is not altogether unlikely that, some thousands of years from now, ice will again begin to accumulate in Canada and advance southward. The story of the Pleistocene may not be over.

NINE

THE AGE OF MAN

The earth does not belong to man, man belongs to the earth.

(Inscription on U.S. Pavilion at Expo '74, Spokane, Washington)

The very last part of Cenozoic time is known as the Age of Man. That human beings are a recent arrival on the earth scene can be emphasized by the following analogy. If all geologic time were compressed into 1 year, the first human being would have appeared at approximately 6:30 P.M. on December 31. And all recorded human history would have occurred after 11:50 P.M. on New Year's Eve. Man barely made it! (For brevity we use *man* to mean "mankind as a whole," with women most certainly included!)

What is man anyway? What distinguishes us from other animals? Without getting involved in a philosophical, religious, or anthropologic discussion, let's use the definition of Dr. Mary Leakey, who said, "I prefer the criterion for 'man' to be based on the establishment of organized tool-making rather than on the morphology of any particular period." This, in practice, means stone tools, for ancient wooden tools would decay and would not likely be preserved.

Man is the most advanced of the primates, those mammals with eyes in the front of the head for depth perception and with fingers and thumb well adapted for grasping and tree climbing. Let's take a brief and sketchy look at the geological history of the human race. There is little agreement on details of man's evolution; what is presented here is to be taken as only one viewpoint.

EARLY MAN

The fossil record of humans and their ancestors is somewhat scanty, as you read in the previous chapter. The first primates (lemurs and tarsiers) appeared in early Cenozoic, about 60 to 65 m.y. ago, and higher primates (apes and monkeys) are present in mid-Cenozoic rocks 30 to 40 m.y. old. The first "prehuman," *Ramapithecus*, with a more semicircular jaw than the elongated apelike jaw, is evidenced as 12-to-14-m.y.-old jaw and tooth fragments from India and East Africa. Then comes an even sketchier part of the fossil record: the transition to "man."

Much knowledge about the "prehistory" of humans has been painstakingly derived over the last century (Figures 9-1 and 9-2). Recent work in East Africa has greatly added to our knowledge of early man. Anthropologists Louis and Mary Leakey spent decades of patient searching at Olduvai Gorge, Tanzania, where primitive stone tools, such as rounded egg-sized chert pebbles with some chips knocked off one end, had been found. Finally, in 1959, they discovered skull and tooth fragments in a valley wall, about 75 meters below the surface. Based on 60 K-Ar age dates from a bed of volcanic ash above the bones, the fragments are at least 1.75 m.y. old. This discovery, named *Zinjanthropus* (now classed as *Australopithecus*, or "near-man" type), was soon followed by finds of "true-man" fossils (*Homo*), just as old but clearly associated with tools.

Richard Leakey, the Leakeys' son, has since discovered at Lake Rudolph, Kenya, 800 kilometers north of Olduvai, skull 1470, which he interprets as another *Homo* type. Its age is 2.8 m.y., again based on K-Ar dating of volcanic ash. This area has yielded hundreds of tools and remains of nearly 100 near-men and true-men.

Interestingly, it appears that *Homo* coexisted for a long time in East Africa with *Australopithecus*. And, whereas some *Australopithecus* types apparently were dead-enders and did not evolve into more human forms, the smaller and more intelligent *Homo* types were probably steps along the way to *Homo sapiens*, our species.

Many other researchers are also working to clarify further the history of early man. An international research team in Ethiopia has recently found the 3-m.y.-old remains of a 3-foot-tall hominid, and claims it is the most complete early-man discovery ever made in Africa. A Harvard team has recently discovered, west of Lake Rudolph, a piece of *Australopithecus* jawbone with a single deeply pitted tooth; this find dates at 5.5 m.y. ago. The search goes on.

Another species, *Homo erectus*, has also been found at several other places. For example, Heidelberg man (Germany) is known by only a lower jaw, found with bones of ancient elephants and rhinos 23 meters below the surface, and is estimated to be 500,000 years old. Peking man was found in China in 1923 in caves with bones of deer, horses, buffalo, rhinos, and boars.

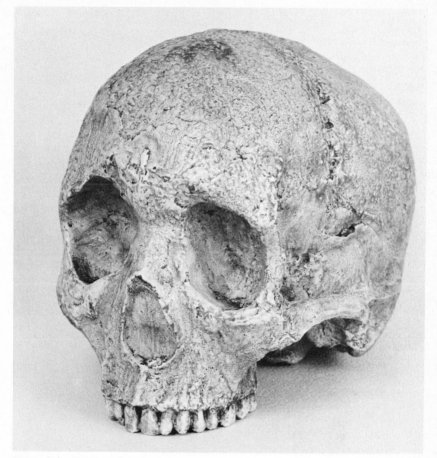

Figure 9-1 Replica of skull of *Homo sapiens sapiens*, from Gamble's Cave, Kenya, an early *Homo sapiens sapiens* site. *(Courtesy of K. Moran.)*

Many skulls were cracked open and the bases widened to get at the brain—cannibals? Unfortunately, the original Peking bones were lost during World War II. Their age is placed at about 400,000 years.

HOMO SAPIENS

The steps between early man and "modern man" (*Homo sapiens*) are difficult to date. Why? Recall that K-Ar dating is only reliable from the distant past up to about as recently as 1 million years ago because of the long half-life of K (little Ar forms in only a million years), and ^{14}C dating is good only from the present back to a maximum of about 50,000 years because of the short half-life of ^{14}C (there is little ^{14}C left to measure). Although new dating techniques show some promise of filling this gap, much reliance must be

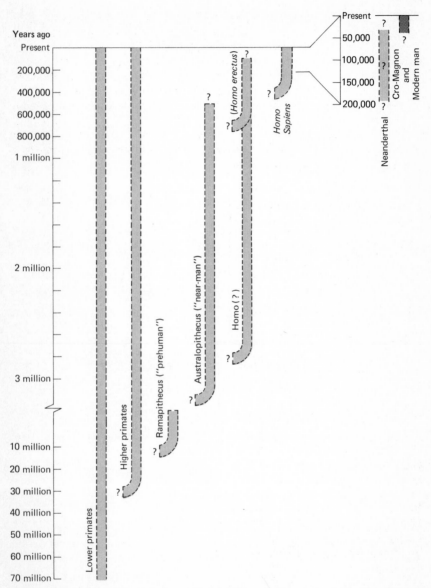

Figure 9-2 The development of man. Note all the question marks, indicating a lack of evidence as to dates. Diagram is highly generalized; consult anthropology texts for greater detail and diverse opinions.

placed on correlation of fossil human remains and tools with the four stages of Pleistocene ice advance and the interglacial stages.

A general guess is that by at least 200,000 years ago, *Homo sapiens* had evolved from *Homo erectus*. Neanderthal man (*Homo sapiens neanderthalensis*), the heavy-boned, hairy and stocky cave man we see pictured so frequently, probably appeared about 100,000 years ago, before the last ice advance. Neanderthal types spread over much of Europe, North Africa, and Asia, hunting mammoths, giant cave bears, and other large mammal species.

The first Neanderthal skeleton was found at Gibraltar in the 1850s and was interpreted to be that of an imbecile who had died of rickets. About the same time, a skeleton in Germany was interpreted as the remains of an old Cossack from the Napoleonic wars; he was stooped because he had been diseased and he had a brow ridge which was the result of his constant

(By permission of Johnny Hart and Field Enterprises, Inc.)

frowning because of the pain he had suffered. Neanderthal finds are abundant. In one cave, 40 smashed skulls were found—cannibalism, ritual, or warfare?

About 40,000 years ago Cro-Magnon man evolved, quite probably from Neanderthal man. He is *Homo sapiens sapiens*, truly modern man, who could not be distinguished from modern people if he were walking on our streets today. The excellent cave paintings up to 20,000 years old in France and Spain are his handiwork. Some of the first ones were discovered on the ceiling of a cave in Spain in 1879 by 5-year old Maria de Sautuola, who wasn't as interested as her father in looking for tools in the material on the floor of the cave.

The fossil record of the human race is not a great one. It is at best only fair, and probably records many branches and dead limbs on our family tree rather than a straight-line main-trunk descent.

The battle over the idea that mankind evolved is perhaps best epitomized by the attack on Thomas Huxley, a friend and defender of Darwin, by Bishop Samuel Wilburforce of Oxford at an 1860 meeting of the British Association for the Advancement of Science. (This was about 6 months after the publication of Darwin's *On the Origin of Species*.) In his concluding remarks, the bishop asked if it was through his grandfather or grandmother that Huxley claimed descent from an ape? Huxley replied that he would not feel ashamed at having an ape for an ancestor, but that he would be ashamed of a brilliant man who argued about scientific matters of which he knew nothing. (That is, he'd prefer an ape, rather than the bishop, for an ancestor.) In the face of ever-mounting evidence the battle has cooled somewhat since those days, but it is, to many people, still a real controversy.

MAN IN NORTH AMERICA

The great glaciers which covered much of northern North America didn't prevent paleohunters from crossing over the Bering Strait from Asia. In fact, sea level was more than 60 meters lower than today because of the water tied up in the glaciers; therefore, much of the present area of the straits would have been exposed as dry land during glacial advances. Some workers have suggested that peoples may have crossed over 26,000 to 28,000 years ago and spread into central North America; a readvance of ice then closed the pathway through Alaska and western Canada, thereby isolating them. These first peoples were the ancestors of the Plains Indians. About 10,000 years ago, a new invasion from Asia may have brought the ancestors of the Eskimos and the Aleut Indians of the northern latitudes. The oldest definite ^{14}C dates on humans in North America are about 12,000 years old. This may be a function of not finding good datable material; for example, charcoal is better than bone. Some workers think these are quite young dates, and that some of the fluted Folsom projectile points may be much older than 12,000 years. Woolly mammoths and reindeer probably entered North America between 100,000 and 50,000 years ago, and human beings may have followed them across the Bering Strait.

Many of these large mammals are extinct in North America, and have been for 5000 to 10,000 years. Why? If the extinctions were due to climatic changes at the retreat of the last glaciers, as has commonly been assumed, then there should have been simultaneous extinction of some smaller mammals and plants, too. Maybe there were, but the scanty fossil record doesn't indicate this to be the case. Also, why were there so many extinctions after the last ice withdrawal and apparently not many after the previous three? Could humans, by excessive hunting pressure, have caused their extinction? Simple overkill may seem improbable, especially so long before the advent of modern weapons. An interesting hypothesis regarding the effects of humans has been proposed. Kill-site evidence indicates that the paleo-Indians preyed largely on the bison and the mammoth. What if carnivores specializing on these animals were starved out during winter competition with the hunters and became extinct? Without those carnivores around to eat their share of young bison, for example, the bison might have expanded in numbers. Such an expansion might have put additional pressure on the grasslands and could have caused extinction of other herbivores who filled the same ecological niches. As these other herbivores died off, so would other carnivores who relied on those species for their food. Thus, a chain reaction may have been initiated by the hunters, and this may have been a factor in the extinction of several large mammals including the mammoth, mastadon, camel, ground sloth, a long-horned bison, and horse. (Horses were reintroduced by the Spaniards in the early 1500s; again humans affected North American ecology!)

MAN TODAY AND TOMORROW

Population (People Pollution?)   It has been estimated that about 8000 B.C., about the time agriculture began, the world had a population of about 5 million *Homo sapiens*. The estimated time required then for the world's population to double was 1500 years, and by the time of Christ, earth had about 200 to 300 million people. By A.D. 1650, the population was 500 million, and it doubled to 1 billion in the next 200 years. The next doubling occurred in 80 years, and by 1930, 2 billion of us were inhabiting this earth (Ehrlich et al., 1973). The doubling time is now only about 35 years; there are now more than 3.8 billion *Homo sapiens* around and we are adding 70 million to our population each year. So quite soon, shortly after 2000, we will number 7 billion! After 15 doublings from now (525 years), at the present doubling rate of about 35 years, there will be one person standing on each square meter of land surface. Someone has calculated that 900 years from now, there will be 100 people per square meter of land and sea area. Moving about would be difficult. Well, we all know that we don't have to worry about such absurd population densities. Starvation, disease, or war will surely keep our numbers at much lower levels.

We hear every day about preservation of environment, about the energy crunch, or about the depletion of other mineral resources. These are indeed problems, but their solutions may prove to be exercises in futility unless the larger, more basic problem—that of population—is not solved soon. Even if

By permission of Johnny Hart and Field Enterprises, Inc.)

the United States and the Western World control population growth and attain ZPG (zero population growth), the population impact of the rest of the world will severely affect us, too. The old expression "The rich get richer and the poor get children" is one which the affluent West should pay heed to, for these people will all add to the pressure on the world's resources. Yet it has also been pointed out that each child born in the United States will use so much more of earth's resources than children born elsewhere that a decline in our population growth has a more immediate effect on the global resource picture than does a population decrease in an underdeveloped nation.

Ecological studies indicate that when a species overpopulates relative to the resources it needs to live, its numbers decrease and the species may even become extinct. Linnaeus, the great classifier of the biological kingdom, said way back in 1753:

> It is true, however, that the most contagious diseases usually rage to a greater degree in thickly populated regions, and I am inclined to think that war occurs when there is the greatest superfluity of people. At least it would seem that, where the population increases too much, concord and the necessities of life decrease, and envy and malignancy towards neighbors abound. Thus it is a war of all against all!

As the National Resource Council of the National Academy of Sciences has stated:

> To delay progress toward full self-regulation of population size is to play Russian roulette with the future of man.

The academy, in a detailed study entitled *Resources and Man* (1969), concluded that the best hope for a comfortable living by our descendants, for a long duration of *Homo sapiens*, and for a high-quality environment is for the earth to have a population less than our present $3\frac{1}{2}$ billion people.

Population growth is simply a function of birth rate versus death rate. To control population, we have two choices; either lower the birth rate or raise the death rate. Do we really have a choice?

Food (Enough?) At least 10,000 people die each day from starvation or related effects (that's nearly 4 million per year!), about one-seventh of the world's people are chronically hungry or starving, and one-half to two-thirds of the world's population is undernourished. We don't seem to be able to produce enough food for our present population, let alone for the annual 70 to 80 million new additions. Assume that the entire annual increment of additional people were born in the United States; could even the United States, the greatest food producer in the world, produce enough food to feed people equivalent to a new United States every 3 years? Not for long.

Yet if the present world food supply were well managed and well distributed to underdeveloped as well as developed countries, it *might* supply just enough calories for the present population. This would mean, of course, that the affluent people of the world, in particular those of the United States, would have to eat less than most of us are accustomed to. And to feed the projected world population of 1985, even at the inadequate 1965 level, would require a total increase of about 50 percent over 1965 production (Ehrlich et al., 1973).

How can we increase food production? Not too long ago we heard the optimistic prediction that oceans would feed the world. This is now known to be a false hope. Most marine life is on the continental shelves, and two-thirds of the ocean is too deep for abundant life. Probably the *very most* we could do with fish production is to double it, and to attempt this could lead to catastrophe. For example, new sonar methods of locating herring schools in the vicinity of the Shetland Islands north of Scotland were employed on 300 fishing ships in 1966. By 1969, the industry was wiped out: the fish were gone because even the smaller immature herring were taken by the new methods (Ehrlich et al., 1973). What about utilizing the less palatable but abundant microscopic forms of life in the seas? We would use as much as or more energy harvesting them than we would get in return. Besides, while seafood is good protein, it contains few calories. Today the seas provide 2 percent of the food energy requirements of mankind and at best might provide 3 percent (National Academy of Sciences, 1969).

How can we increase food production from our lands? One possibility is increasing the area under cultivation. For various reasons, more than 80 percent of earth's land cannot be cultivated; 9 percent is in crops, and another 9 percent has potential. In Europe and Asia, 80 to 90 percent of arable land is cultivated already, and in much of South America, Africa, and Australia either the soil is of low quality or the climate is too dry. And there are problems with opening up new land to cultivation. For example, clearing tropical forests and farming the land results in its transformation in just a few years to "hard red brick." Clearing nontropical forests would result in more acreage for crops, but forest soils are soon depleted of their nutrients, and other ecological problems commonly result. To utilize semiarid or arid areas would require tremendous quantities of water, which would generally have to come from expensive desalting of ocean water. The best hope for expansion of acreage is in North America and the U.S.S.R., where one-half to two-thirds of the arable land, respectively, is under cultivation, but even here the best soils, the prairie soils, are already in use. Yet if all modern technology and knowledge could be applied, with cost not a factor, earth's arable land area could be doubled and the crops might feed a population 10 times that of today (Revelle, 1974). But why push earth and mankind to such limits?

An allied problem is that while we may strive to put more land under cultivation, some of the best lands are being taken out of production by urban sprawl. By 1980, one-third of California's best land will be under lawn and concrete; by 1960, 3 million acres of California farmland had been lost in this way (Ehrlich et al., 1973). This vegetable and fruit basket of the United States may soon not even be able to feed her own burgeoning population.

Crops grown on soil are directly related to climate, and as we learned in Chapter 4, climate is the most important factor governing the processes of chemical weathering of rock and hence the formation of soil. Regions with moderate rainfall and moderate temperatures—the temperate zone—have the best soils. In regions of low rainfall or low temperatures, little chemical weathering occurs. In regions of high rainfall and high temperatures—the tropics—there is too much and too rapid chemical weathering and the nutrients are removed from the soil. In some areas, such as Java, more than a foot of rich soil can form on glassy volcanic ash in only 50 years, but in most regions, the soil forming process takes thousands of years.

Plants, and thus the creatures that eat them, get their nutrients from certain clay minerals and from decaying vegetation; thus, some climatic regions produce nutritious plants and other regions produce less nutritious plants. For example, corn, which grows in the temperate zones, is a low-bulk and high-nutrition food, whereas the banana, which grows on poorer subtropical to tropical soils, is a high-bulk and low-nutrition food. The three most important crops in the world are rice, wheat, and corn, which are all relatively high in protein. Wheat and rice provide 40 percent of all human food energy. Potatoes, plus many crops grown in the tropics, are low-protein foods. Many food experts are now saying that people, rather than animals, should eat the grains. Cattle, sheep, and hogs use 7 calories of food for each calorie of meat they produce; the direct use of grains which they eat would help the food shortage somewhat. Range-fed beef, of course, would obtain their feed from land which cannot be used for growing crops.

All soils are vulnerable; humans can really spoil the soil by overuse without replacing the nutrients. Even with fertilization, some studies indicate that the fertility of Iowa's soil is slowly decreasing. And adding too much fertilizer can result in the carrying off of many of the nutrients by running water, causing lakes to be choked with plant growth. Thus, in attempting to solve one problem, we generate others.

Can the "green revolution" of new high-yield plants help? Yes, the results have been encouraging: world cereal-grain production doubled between 1951 and 1971 (Revelle, 1974). However, there could be related dangers. As pointed out by Ehrlich et al. (1973), we had better store away stocks of seeds of the long-used, older varieties, for if the new, high-yield varieties prove to be susceptible to insects and diseases which the older varieties resisted, we could find the world's food supplies literally wiped out overnight. And ecological factors are involved: the green revolution required a 300 percent increase in pesticides, as well as the use of much more fertilizer and energy.

And climate, besides being the important factor in soil formation, can also be a short-term factor. For several years, we have been quite fortunate, but just one really bad year for crops could be an international disaster. Even the relatively mild droughts of 1974 in the United States decreased the anticipated (August projections) wheat crop by 7.6 percent, the soybean crop by 6.4 percent, and the corn crop by 6.3 percent; Minnesota's corn yield fell from 93 bushels per acre in 1973 to 61 in 1974. Only North America and Australia produce food surpluses; crop failures in these two places could literally be deadly. And, we don't even have a good surplus of grains in storage anymore. The world's increasing population has decreased the reserves. In the fall of 1974, for example, world grain reserves were equal to only a 27-day supply (Revelle, 1974); 13 years before, the world had a 95-day reserve.

Longer-term climatic changes could be even more important. The world has had optimum growing conditions for the last half-century, possibly the best in the last 1000 years, according to some experts. Now the world's climate seems to be cooling, and if so, this will mean shorter growing seasons and shorter food supplies.

New technology and equipment may not be the answer either, for it already takes $1\frac{1}{2}$ calories of fossil fuels to produce and process each calorie of food produced in the United States (Ehrlich et al., 1973). And as we have recently been made aware, the fossil fuels are in short supply. So, can we afford to fertilize and irrigate poorer lands and to further develop our technology? If so, maybe we can significantly increase our acreage, but the food will be costly and the limitations are real.

The basic problem is *not* food production: it is people production. To paraphrase *Project Survival* (1970), men and women are like cancer cells that do not know when to stop multiplying. Say it were economically, socially, and technologically possible to increase earth's food supply by eight or ten times; a century from now, with our projected population, each person would get the same poor average food allotment he or she gets today. Two-thirds of the people would still be undernourished.

So, the green revolution and all the related technological advances may be too late. Norman Borlaug, who developed "miracle wheats" and improved rice plants and won the Nobel Peace Prize in 1970, said that the green revolution has only delayed the world food crisis for another 30 years, and that if world population continues to increase at the same rate, "we will destroy the species." He said that in 1970, and it will probably take birth control measures, even without any opposition, more than 20 years to bring reproduction under control. Therefore, more starvation will come soon. Yet the 1974 United Nations World Population Conference in Bucharest, Romania, voted *not* to recommend a worldwide reduction in family size (Figure 9-3). There are many estimates as to when we'll starve. Paddock and Paddock, in *Famine—1975!* show a graph based on world wheat production and consumption; the production and consumption curves cross at 1975 (famine) or at 1985 (famine) depending upon the estimates. But such estimates may be way off. Perhaps we won't starve until the year 2000, which is still years off in the future.

Preservation of Environment   Pollution of our environment is a problem about which nearly everyone gets emotional. The extreme conservationist says, "Industry be damned—close them down." An extremist on the other side might say, "No industry means no jobs. Environment be damned." As someone once said, "Minds are like parachutes—they only function when they are open." Obviously, the extreme positions on this matter generally pose no solutions; certain trade-offs are necessary. We should be able, with proper planning, to have our cake and yet be able to eat it, too. For example, mining must go on more than ever with our present shortages. Yet it must be done with a minimum of environmental disturbance.

Whether we already have a perilously polluted planet may be debatable, but we have indeed caused a deterioration of virtually all aspects of our environment. Air and water pollution may not always be readily apparent, but improper disposal of solid wastes is easily observed. Each American generates 6 pounds of solid trash per day. Farms may add at least 10 times as much waste as all people combined, but fortunately much of this can be recycled. The amount of solid waste generated by industry is undoubtedly huge, but is difficult to estimate. We have covered much of our world with rubbish.

Our air in the big metropolitan areas, but to an extent even the air in the most remote areas, carries gaseous and particulate pollutants. Industry is guilty, but some studies show that, in the United States, automobiles contribute three to four times as much air pollution as does industry.

Figure 9-3 *(Courtesy of Jerry Fearing and St. Paul Dispatch.)*

Our waters are certainly polluted. Industry has so charged some water-ways with wastes that rivers in our industrial centers have on occasion actually burned! In the past, municipalities haven't exactly helped the purity of our water, either. And even a relatively few people in the wilderness can pollute waters. For example, the wilderness Boundary Waters Canoe Area of

YOU SHOULDN'T RAPE OUR NATURAL RESOURCES LIKE THAT!

IT'S ONLY A WILDFLOWER.

ONLY A WILDFLOWER! WHAT IF EVERYONE IN THE WORLD WENT OUT AND PICKED A WILDFLOWER TODAY!

SO WE WOULD HAVE LOST 15 WILDFLOWERS! WHAT'S THE PROBLEM?

(Courtesy of Employee Publication Art, Los Angeles, Calif.)

Minnesota received 97,600 visits (632,500 visitor days of 12 hours each) in 1966. In 1974, the figure was 163,429 visits and 1,061,130 visitor days. This "people pressure," even in a 4167-square-kilometer (1600-square-mile) wilderness area, has caused the closing of numerous overused campsites and has so polluted the waters in many lakes that they are no longer drinkable (Figure 9-4). These problems are the result of overuse, especially along certain canoe routes, and not necessarily misuse. However, littering in this same area recently necessitated a ban on all cans and bottles; this problem is clearly due to misuse by unthinking, ignorant, or stupid people. People pressure is also affecting many of our parks (Figure 9-5).

Why are our water and air so polluted? Largely because people have always had the philosophy that the waterways and airways were "bottomless sinks" for our solid, chemical, and thermal wastes (Figure 9-6). The sinks have now become clogged, and we'll have to spend much time, effort, and money to unclog them and keep them clear. In retrospect, this bottomless-sink philosophy seems especially strange, since these water and air sinks have also been the sources of our drinking water and our oxygen.

We are still using 70 percent of the earth's surface—the oceans—as a big sink. Is this sink so large that it will never be ruined? No, it is already polluted; international regulation is necessary to assure its healthy survival. This pollution can affect the marine life cycle, and if this cycle is disrupted it will also affect life cycles on land, including that of human beings.

But we can clean up our air and waters if we really want to. Two classic water examples are the Thames River, which flows through London, and the Willamette River in Oregon. The former, after 200 years in which no fish could live in it, now sports numerous species, and the Willamette, after decades without a fall chinook salmon run, is again a place to catch this fish. London and Pittsburgh, as well as other cities, have markedly cleaned their air. "Solid" pollution is certainly something which each and every one of us can work at every day (Figure 9-7).

And all this preservation-of-environment action is not just to ensure the beauty of our surroundings, either, for it can head off larger problems. For example, too much carbon dioxide in the air can even change earth's climate by creating a warming, greenhouse effect; the CO_2 of the atmosphere absorbs solar energy, which is reradiated from the ground, and in turn part of this heat is reradiated back to earth. (People have increased the CO_2 content of the atmosphere more than 10 percent in the last century by burning fossil fuels.) It is very possible that the addition of heat in this manner could cause the world's present glaciers to melt, thereby raising sea level 30 to 60 meters

Figure   9-4 Overuse. Sign in BWCA (Boundary Waters Canoe Area), Minnesota.

and drowning the seaports and coastlines of the world. It is also theoretically possible that heating the earth's atmosphere by a small amount could result in an unfrozen Arctic Ocean, hence more evaporation and precipitation (snow) in the far north, and hence snow accumulation and a new glacial advance. Either way, we would have a real environmental problem! There may be some people who will say, "So what?" A glacial retreat or advance will probably occur eventually anyway, man or no man. With four major glacial advances and retreats in the past 1 million years or so and with the last retreat only 10,000 to 15,000 years ago, is there any reason to think the Ice Age is over?

Depletion of Mineral Resources   The United States, with only 6 percent of the world's population, uses about 30 percent of the natural resources removed from the earth each year. For example, each American uses an average of 1 ton of iron and 18 pounds of copper per year, whereas people in the rest of the world average 0.17 tons of iron and 3.2 pounds of copper. C. F. Park of Stanford University has written a prophetic book entitled *Affluence*

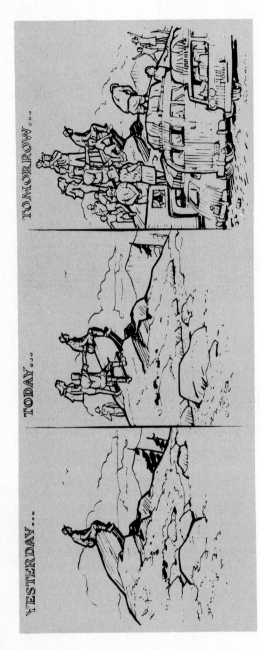

Figure 9-5 People pressure. This illustration, drawn in 1967, did not anticipate the energy crisis, which first hit us in 1974. Therefore, people pressure may be alleviated a bit by the high cost and shortage of fuel. *(Reprinted from Burdened acres—the people problem, by R. Wendolin with drawing by Monroe Bush, in The Living Wilderness, Spring–Summer 1967, edited by M. Nadel. By permission of the Wilderness Society, Washington, D.C.)*

(a)

(b)

Figure 9-6 Our polluted water and our polluted air. Not too many years ago there was a lack of concern about pollution, but now rapid strides are being made to correct the situation.

Figure 9-7 Scenic view in a roadside park.

in Jeopardy (1968). To put it simply, Americans will soon have to get used to a lower material standard of living, whether we like it or not. To paraphrase Park a bit further, we will need twice as much iron and copper in the year 2000 on the basis of projections of present rates of use and population growth. If the rest of the world's material standard of living is to reach our present standards, by the year 2000 we will have to mine annually about 12 times as much iron and copper as is now being mined. (And this assumes *our* use of these metals will not increase.)

Is that great an increase even possible? The highest-grade ore deposits have already been mined, and most high-grade deposits have probably been already discovered. According to T. S. Lovering, the entire mineral production of the world before World War II was about equal to what has been used since. We are, with improved technology, able to mine lower- and lower-grade deposits, but as the grade lowers, the cost of production generally goes up. And, this requires a greater use of energy resources. There are limits to what is feasible. Only iron, out of all the metals, is present on earth in good supply; our known iron reserves are enough to last several hundred years. But, obtaining a sufficient supply of nearly all other metals will pose a problem in the very near to relatively near future, depending upon the metal in question. For example, some experts predict that the world's supply of mercury, tin, and tungsten will be used up by the year 2000.

How can we prevent mineral shortages? Is recycling of scrap metals an answer? Yes, but only a partial answer. Substitutions of one material for another may help with some commodities, but generally will probably be only a minor factor. Will more mining of low-grade deposits (the average igneous rock consists of 8 percent aluminum and 5 percent iron), utilizing improved technology, be the answer to our problems? Probably not, because of the great amounts of energy which must be expended to utilize lower-grade deposits. It has been estimated that if the United States had to depend upon obtaining metals from scrap and from common rocks, it would have a difficult time maintaining the material standard of living of a century ago.

The answer to the shortages must, of necessity, be in holding down the demand for these materials, and this means maintaining a reasonable population. Even then, the shortages will exist. As the National Research Council of the National Academy of Sciences concluded in their *Resources and Man* study (1969), referring to future shortages, "Only our best efforts in all phases of resource management and population control can *defer* that day."

The problem is real, even for affluent Americans. Since just before World War II, the United States has consumed in total more of 18 critical minerals (12 metals plus fluorspar, phosphate, cement, gypsum, potassium, and sulfur) than it has produced, and has of necessity relied on imports (Cameron, 1973). In 1970, we imported more than half of our metals, and our production and consumption gap is widening. In 1930, the United States used half of the world's production of the 18 important minerals referred to above; by 1970, we used less than 20 percent. Obviously, the competition for these commodities has been increasing and will continue to increase. Bearing world social and political issues in mind, it may well be prudent for the United States to become more self-sufficient in all raw materials, as has been suggested so emphatically by Cameron. The Department of Interior has recently predicted that by the year 2000, the United States may have an annual gap of $100 billion between the value of our mineral requirements and our internal production of these minerals. This would have a strong negative effect on our balance of trade.

Energy Problems   Until the last century muscles were the main source of energy. Then the burning of wood became the major source, until many forests of the world were exhausted. Whale oil had become the major fuel for lighting, but by the 1850s, we were already experiencing an energy crisis because of the drastically decreased numbers of whales; whale oil was selling for $2.50 a gallon! Fortunately, the discovery of oil in Romania in 1858 and in Pennsylvania in 1859 solved that one. However, it was coal that largely replaced wood as an energy source; by 1900, nearly 90 percent of the energy generated in the United States was from coal, and by 1905, petroleum was still supplying only 10 percent. With further industrialization and modernization, oil and gas assumed the lead, and by 1973, 76 percent of the United States' energy and 65 percent of the world's energy was from this source.

As with metals, the United States uses more energy than any other nation. Although we have only 6 percent of the people, we use a third of the world's energy, and Canada is second to us in energy use per capita. Every day each American uses 4 gallons of oil, 300 cubic feet of natural gas and 15 pounds of coal. To put that in perspective, a 100-watt-bulb burning for 10 hours uses 1 kilowatt-hour of electricity, which costs us about 3 cents; a cup of oil ($\frac{1}{16}$ gallon) must be burned to produce that kilowatt. All the other people in the world average only one-eigth as much. And American demand for electricity for industry and living is rapidly increasing; estimates of how much energy we will need by the year 2000 vary from three to seven times the present demand.

A computer simulation has indicated that if every one of the 150 or so nations used oil at the same rate as the developed world is using it the world's entire known supply would be used up by 1982!

Where does the oil and gas come from? American production peaked about 1970; the (1976) United States imports total about 30 percent of the nation's needs, and by 1985, unless we drastically increase our own production, we shall be importing 60 percent of the total, perhaps as much as 5 billion barrels (42 gallons per barrel) a year! We shall probably have to increase our exports of other items by about 50 percent just to keep our international balance of payments in decent shape. We produce about 10 million barrels of oil a day in the 48 states from about 240 large and 14,000 small fields and probably will add 2 million barrels per day with the Alaskan production. As our projected requirements by 1985 range from about 25 million barrels per day to over 60 million barrels per day, we can't possibly produce all our own needs. (Note also that Alaska's oil is not a really big factor in the picture.) We have hopes for future production from our eastern continental shelf, but this is as yet only a hope; we haven't yet put down a single drill hole to really test the potential. Therefore, we are dependent upon the rest of the world for an important part of our supply.

The known oil reserves of the world are largely concentrated in the Middle East, where from half to two-thirds of the reserves exist. Northern Africa and the Communist bloc each have about 15 percent. The United States' reserves, including Alaska's, are only 5 percent, and the Western Hemisphere's total is only about 12 percent. And, since oil and gas are the only energy sources which we can use to quickly plug the energy gap, we are obviously going to be concerned with world politics, especially with regards to the Middle East, for some time to come.

Yet, in terms of human history, the world's petroleum problems are relatively short-lived. The oil produced since 1965 is about equal to all the oil produced before that time! We will probably have used most of the world's natural gas in a few more decades; it is half gone now, and proven United States' reserves will last only 13 years at the present rate of use. We will use most of the world's oil by about 2025; it is one-quarter gone now, and the middle 80 percent will be used between 1967 and 2023. The United States automobile alone would use up all our nation's reserves in about 10 years, assuming the same annual growth rate in number of autos as in 1973 (MacDonald, 1974). Most of the oil from oil shale, if we can develop it, may be used up by about 2025 or 2100. The world has much coal and only a few percent of the total has been used; at the present rates of consumption, it could last 300 to 500 years. But 80 percent of the world's coal may be gone within a few hundred years, especially if we don't change our wasteful ways and have to use it heavily in place of our dwindling petroleum supplies.

The above figures, largely from Hubbert (1974), show clearly that we *Homo sapiens* are living in the "fossil-fuel epoch" of human history, an epoch that will last about 300 years in all. In the future, our descendants may well shake their heads in utter disbelief as they ponder the fact that those idiots (us!) used the world's oil, gas, and coal as fuel, rather than saving it for chemicals. By the way, fossil fuels form slowly; most are tens of millions to hundreds of millions of years old. They are therefore irreplaceable during the Age of Man.

Yet the world's automobiles and power plants are doubling in number every 10 years! This is not, of course, too compatible with diminishing fossil-fuel supplies. Since oil and gas are apparently short-timers, what can we do to stretch out their life-spans? Now, because of the current energy crisis, we may have awakened to the reality of the situation. Many proposals have been made to conserve fuel. As 25 percent of our total energy consumption (half of all petroleum) goes for transportation, mass transit is often cited as a must. It will surely help, but a Shell study has shown that it will mainly affect intracity transportation and would reduce car use and gasoline consumption by only 3 to 4 percent, in spite of the fact that 70 percent of United States residents live in the city. The answer must be a broader one: "Energy conservation must become an integral part of future energy policy," stated Senator Henry Jackson, Chairman of the Committee on Interior and Insular Affairs, United States Senate. Indeed, it must, and soon!

Our "policy" has, in fact, been quite the opposite. We've encouraged increased energy consumption, we've encouraged the shift from coal to natural gas by regulating a low price at well heads (from 1961 to 1971, natural gas demand increased 75 percent) and thereby making it more economical than coal, and we've had a hodgepodge of 67 governmental agencies and 12 Congressional committees involved with energy matters! We now have a new Federal Energy Administration, which should be an improvement. Our government is finally funding research and development; we are now cranking up in the fields of nuclear, geothermal, and solar energy, oil-shale processing, and gasification of coal. Industry is working at problems, too; 15 companies have contributed $500,000 each for a joint research project on oil shale, which is already commercial at our present inflated prices. A major problem is what to do with the waste rock from the process; its volume is up to twice its original volume. Furthermore, processing the oil shales requires great quantities of water, which aren't available in our semiarid West, where the oil shale is found. A recent hope is removal of the oil by bacterial action; the oil shale would be fractured in place and then flushed out without any necessity of mining.

Our coal industry, which has deteriorated for the last few decades, must be made healthy again, and ways must be found to utilize the abundant high-sulfur coals without damaging our air. "Trade-offs" will be necessary here, for to mine coal, which occurs as widespread but thin layers, requires strip-mining; this will alter the landscape to a degree, and to burn coal will cause some pollution. As S. David Freeman, Director of the Ford Foundation Energy Policy Project, said, "There are two things wrong with coal today. We can't mine it and we can't burn it." (Hammond, Metz, and Maugh, 1973.) The earth's coal reserves total many trillion tons; the United States has reserves of at least 400 billion tons.

What about other sources? The gasification of coal is an unproven process as yet and requires much water, as does the process which removes petroleum from oil shale. Waterpower cannot be greatly increased; our most likely rivers already have many hydroelectric plants on them. However, some have suggested that cloud-seeding projects could perhaps be utilized to increase water supplies, and, in turn, more dams and power plants might be feasible. Harnessing tidal energy may have some potential as a minor energy source, but probably only locally along coastlines. Geothermal heat from hot spring areas is harnessed at a few places in the world, but only at one locality in the United States: northern California. However, future research involving the drilling of holes deep into the earth's crust where the geothermal gradient is high, pumping water into them, and utilizing the heat from this water as it rises as steam may prove feasible. A few other minor energy sources have also been suggested. Converting garbage into oil or gas (some estimate the oil yield could be from 3 to 18 percent of the United States oil demand), conversion of cow manure into gas, burning wastes as fuel in power plants, and utilizing windmills as our ancestors did are just some of the suggestions. Each would help, but obviously none is the total answer.

Nuclear power today supplies only a few percent of our energy, but some experts predict that by 1980 it may provide 25 percent and by 1990, 50 percent. This energy is a product of nuclear fission, or the splitting of atomic nuclei, the principle of the A-bomb. (Recall that Einstein's atomic formula, $E = mc^2$, shows that the energy given off by a small transformed mass, m, is fantastically large because the quantity of mass is multiplied by the speed of light, c, squared. Only 150 grams of thorium, for example, yields as much energy as 400 metric tons of coal or 2000 barrels of crude oil.)

To date, we can use only one of the atomic isotopes, uranium 235, as fuel in our burner reactors; this isotope constitutes less than 1 percent of natural uranium. However, it is possible to bombard ^{238}U and ^{232}Th, to produce the isotopes ^{239}Pl and ^{233}Th, which can then be used as nuclear fuel. This process, known as the conversion, or breeder, reaction, must be perfected soon, as we are rapidly burning the ^{235}U which is necessary as the ignition system for the breeder process. We hope to have this process commercial by 1985.

As M. King Hubbert said in 1969:

The energy potentially obtainable by breeder reactions from rocks occurring at mineable depths in the United States and containing 50 grams or more of uranium and thorium combined per metric ton is hundreds or thousands of times larger than that of all the fossil fuels combined. It is clear, therefore, that by the transition to a complete breeder-reaction program before the initial supply of U^{235} is exhausted, very much larger supplies of energy can be made available than now exist. Failure to make this transition could constitute one of the major disasters in human history.

High-grade uranium deposits are scarce, but many widely distributed rock units such as some black shales and some granitic plutons are essentially low-grade ores and contain large quantities of uranium or thorium. According to data from the United States Atomic Energy Commission (now the Energy Research and Development Administration), world demand for uranium is expected to increase at an average rate of 15 percent per year for the next 20 years. This is a greater increase than any other mineral has ever undergone, and it will require many geologists and great expenditures to keep up with demand.

As we know, however, disposal of the nuclear wastes from the fission process is a serious problem. The actual amount of wastes can be small. When solidified, the annual wastes from a 1-million-kilowatt nuclear power plant can be compressed into 1 cubic meter. But, what do we do with it?

The other type of nuclear reaction is *nuclear fusion*, the joining together of atomic nuclei; this is the principle of the H-bomb. For example, when four hydrogen nuclei (each consisting only of a proton) join to make a helium nucleus (two protons and two neutrons), the resultant mass of helium is slightly less than that of the four original hydrogen nuclei. Some matter has been "lost," or transformed into energy during the nuclear reaction. (The energy is again given by $E = mc^2$.) The fusion process utilizing the fusion of two heavy hydrogen (deuterium) nuclei (each with one proton and one neutron) may offer the most promise as a future energy source. Deuterium constitutes only 0.015 percent of all hydrogen, but the amount in only 1 cubic kilometer of seawater can give off as much energy as the world's ultimate oil supply! And if the deuterium content of the seas were reduced by only 1 percent, the energy provided would be 500,000 times the world's *total* fossil fuel supply (Hubbert, 1969). The process has not been perfected, unless one accepts "perfection" in the form of an H-bomb, for it involves such high temperatures that all known substances vaporize. Its use as an energy source may still be decades in the future, but the energy yield is worth a great expenditure on research and technology. Besides, no dangerous waste products are produced by nuclear fusion.

Many experts say that solar energy will be the ultimate pollution-free answer to our energy problem. It already drives the natural cycles on earth—rain, wind, oceans, life—and is the original energy source for even our fossil fuels. Solar energy is already feasible on a homeowner scale, but a backup heating system is still necessary because of the energy storage problem to carry over sunless periods. However, with today's methods, solar energy on a large scale is about 100 times as costly as conventional power. With a major technological breakthrough in this area, perhaps we could really utilize this fantastic energy source. Tiny earth receives only a very, very small fraction of the sun's total radiation, but even this amount is equal to about 1.5×10^{18} kilowatt-hours (1,515,000 billion kilowatt-hours) each year. By way of contrast, the 3663 electric plants in the United States generated, in all of 1974, 1.55×10^{12} kilowatt-hours (1550 billion kilowatt-hours). Thus the sun provides the world with nearly a million times as much energy as does the United States, which produces more than a third of the energy generated by people.

There is no question about one thing: We must start conserving energy. In the future, nuclear, solar, and geothermal energy will probably be our main sources of energy, but their development as major contributors is still decades away. Some experts predict that we will not have breeder reactors until the year 1990, that fusion reactors will not be available before 2010, and that solar energy may not be a big factor before 2020. We must be sure we stretch out our petroleum to carry us until then.

Gift of the Past, Problem of the Present, Challenge of the Future
(*Inscription on Energy Pavilion, Expo '74, Spokane, Washington*)

CONCLUDING STATEMENT

We've already stated that human beings are a very late arrival on the planet Earth. Good arguments could be made for saying that the earth would have been better off if the human race had missed its connections and had never evolved. *Homo sapiens* is the only creature on earth with the ability and capacity to change the earth, for better or for worse. Without people, the earth could be a really nice place in which to live. But we are here. . . . How will we handle our responsibilities?

We have food problems, pollution problems, and natural resource problems, and all are accentuated by the population problem. We have wrongly equated human "progress" with economic growth. In a book entitled *The Limits to Growth* (Meadows et al., 1972), by the Club of Rome and a Massachusetts Institute of Technology project team, an integrated computer study of five factors—population, agricultural production, natural resources, industrial production, and pollution—shows that if the present trends continue, limits to growth will come within about 100 years. Then the world will suffer "a sudden and uncontrollable decline" in population and industrial capacity—chaos! The authors of that study said the alternative is to develop and institute a world growth policy immediately. To wait until the year 2000 may be too late to alter future trends.

A more sophisticated computer analysis, dividing the world into 10 interacting geographic-political-social regions rather than considering it as a single system, is a recent approach to the world crises (Mesarovic and Pestel, 1974, *Mankind At The Turning Point,* the Second Report to the Club of Rome). Individual regions may collapse, affecting all other regions. If world-wide planning doesn't take place, each region will ultimately collapse in turn. To ward off such regional collapses, a controlled growth is called for, meaning among other things, investment aid provided by the developed world to the developing world. The study concludes that the current crises are not temporary, that solutions must be global in scale with a new world economic order and a global resources allocation system, and that the solutions must encompass all aspects of mankind's existence. But optimistically, they do conclude that the world crises can be resolved by cooperation. The year 2000 may not be too late, either; but delays make the solutions tremendously more costly. They also point out what we as individuals can do: We can (must?) develop a world consciousness and concern for people everywhere, a conservation ethic, a more harmonious relationship with our natural surroundings, and a sense of identification with generations yet unborn.

M. King Hubbert (1969) has emphasized that the present period of great (exponential) industrial growth is part of a transitory period of fossil-fuel exploitation only about 3 centuries long, between two very long periods of essentially no growth. That growth cannot continue indefinitely should be obvious to all.

Senator Abraham Ribicoff of Connecticut has stated:

> To begin with we must recognize that we . . . can no longer follow a policy dedicated solely to national growth. Second, we must recognize . . . (that) so long as our population and production increases, we will never reduce our pollution.
>
> So we will need a new economics which rewards the man who preserves more, not only the man who produces more. And we will need a new environmental ethic which emphasizes the dependence of man on nature, not his domination over it.

We have even heard recently that if the United States attains ZPG, our economy will suffer too drastically. Again, we are attuned to the growth ethic of the past century. Perhaps we can concentrate upon coming up with a healthy and stabilized economy instead. We cannot think only of short-term answers, for the problems will not vanish even if we manage to be fat and happy for a few decades more. Our children and grandchildren will be stuck with the same problems and with less chance of solving them at that time than we now have. Problems like our present energy crisis can be beneficial. We have lived long, especially in the United States, on cheap and abundant energy, and this crisis has shown us that now we must start planning.

Some refute all these "problems" as the work of doomsters and argue against the quoted statistics. So what if the estimates are wrong with regard to population, resources, and all? What if a given resource will last 200 years, instead of the projected 50 years? Will the extra 150 years make any real difference to the human race a few generations from now?

We have learned an important axiom of geology: "The present is the key to the past." It now seems that the numerous students who have misquoted the principle of uniformitarianism in geology exams really hit on an axiom of utmost importance to humanity: "The present is the key to the future."

Like as the waves make towards the pebbled shore,
So do our minutes hasten to their end.

William Shakespeare (Sonnet 60)

INDEX

Page numbers in *italic* indicate reference to illustrations.